Managing Technology for Competitive Advantage
Integrating technological and organisational development:
from strategy to action

Managing Technology for Competitive Advantage

Integrating technological and organisational development: from strategy to action

Brian Twiss · Mark Goodridge

PITMAN PUBLISHING
128 Long Acre, London WC2E 9AN

A Division of Longman Group UK Limited

First published in Great Britain 1989

© Brian Twiss and Mark Goodridge 1989

A CIP record for this book is available from the British Library

ISBN 0 273 02955 X

Printed and bound in Singapore

Contents

List of illustrations and tables

Foreword

Readers of this book have witnessed remarkable change in industry and commerce both nationally and internationally.

In the fifties and sixties the steel industry gradually got into difficulties whilst its major customers grew in technical competence and scale. At the same time the chemical industry switched to oil feedstocks and vast petrochemical and pharmaceutical enterprises emerged from this particular technological change.

In the seventies there was a reduction in emphasis on R&D and a rationalisation of resources with more effort on technical service. Painful reorganisation brought mergers and takeovers on the industrial scene. Nevertheless, we can see now that new businesses were forming even during this period of retrenchment. Today change continues at an even faster pace, driven by market opportunity and new technology.

Research in solid state physics and molecular biology done in the fifties generated the current drivers of technical change – microchip technology and biotechnology. Robots, computers and sensors are changing manufacturing productivity and product quality at a fast pace. Biotechnology is making relatively slow progress alongside the chemical industry. Yet both the manufacturing and chemical industries do not find these changes easy to manage. In both fields new technology has led to a crop of small, and in some cases rapidly growing, venture capital companies which can often move much faster than large companies.

The pace of change may be different in different industries but for each company there are two essential questions:

(a) What are the appropriate markets for our new technology?
(b) How can we gain competitive advantage?

As technical or marketing strategies evolve there are inevitably changes in organisation. Each function of a company becomes involved; a sound company copes with technical *revolution* by *evolution*.

Many books have been written on aspects of these complicated developments which affect individual companies. They have tended to concentrate on one industry, one theme or one nation. Several Business Schools have become renowned for their courses on business administration which give overviews and propagate management techniques appropriate to technology–based industries.

Books are difficult to write and courses are difficult to construct because of the sheer complexity of the management of an industrial company. Not only must the technology be developed and commissioned and the markets identified but capital investment, cash flow and skills have to be managed. Ultimately the shareholders and the Stock Exchange have to be satisfied.

The essence of this new book is a balanced account of the interplay of many functions involved in the management of technical change to give competitive advantage. The text draws strength from the fact that it combines the experience of both a technologist and a manager of a company of a size which focussed the interplay of all factors on to a small group of people. The text is for *all* managers and not just for technologists. Technology is too valuable to be left to technical experts! So is the subject matter of this book. It encapsulates the lessons from half a century of change.

Prof. Sir Geoffrey Allen FRS, Director of Research and Engineering
Unilever plc and N.V.
January 1989

Preface

The inspiration of this book comes from a chance meeting of two people who traditionally would have very little in common, but who in practice have a great deal. We come from different strands of business learning: Brian Twiss is a technologist, Mark Goodridge a manager of a small business which works with organisations to help them change. Together we have two strategic strands for competitive advantage: technology and organisational change. It is through binding and integrating these two strands that this book is created.

It is our strong belief that successful businesses *integrate* their thoughts and actions; they *manage* the boundaries between our segmented organisations. This book is about management, managing technology across all its organisational boundaries. We have aimed this book at senior managers, as they can most influence the gaining of competitive advantage from technology.

Our chance meeting was at a seminar held in the University Centre, Cambridge, in the summer of 1983. The seminar was one set up as the start of a Training agency project to develop ideas and approaches to the management of technological change. From this seminar Brian and I found that we are kindred spirits, which led us to work together for four years researching, examining and assisting companies with technological change.

We owe a great deal to the foresight of the then Manpower Services Commission, now the Training agency, which gave us the opportunity to develop our work in change management. Many of the detailed studies and conclusions from this work have now been published by the Training agency. Working together in this way has enabled us to build on our research and practical experience to develop the ideas on which we have written this book. The various projects we have undertaken for the Training agency led us to review technology management in the UK, West Germany and Japan and to work closely with eight major British companies.

The book is aimed at managers and all those wishing to develop their understanding of the dynamics of technology, organisations and change. Throughout the book the reader will find checklists and questions which

we hope will be both thought-provoking and of practical value. We have
reduced wherever possible the amount of 'theory', seeking to make our
points through numerous practical examples.

There are many people we have to thank for making this book possible
particularly; those in the Training Agency who sponsored our research;
managers in various companies who shared with us their experiences and
insights; our colleagues who read and amended our proofs adding their
ideas and suggestions.

We would also like to thank our families for their patience and fore-
bearance during the preparation of this work.

This book is dedicated to Brian's wife Pam and Mark's children
Matthew and Vaila.

Brian Twiss
Mark Goodridge
Cambridge
August 1988

Introduction

All companies face the challenge of new technology, be they in manufac-turing or services. To some extent all businesses are investing in it. Unfortunately these investments are often accompanied by unexpected problems, often resulting in benefits substantially lower than anticipated; sometimes they lead to serious losses.

There is a growing realisation that the adoption of new technology is a highly complex process. Success is dependent not only upon the management of the change in the technology itself but also upon the changes within the business which are necessary to exploit the potential of the technology. It is these technology-induced organisational changes which management often has great difficulty in coming to terms with. Frequently it involves the culture of the business, its strategies, the organ-isational structure, managerial attitudes, and personnel policies. All these elements are interlinked and, like a chain, failure will ensue if one of the links is ineffective.

A great deal can be learnt from the experience of the relatively few firms which have been outstandingly successful in exploiting technical change. There is also a growing number of studies into the management of tech-nological innovation which indicate the factors necessary for success. Why, then, do so many companies experience difficulty? There are two main reasons:

- Most managers are unaware of what is known about the technical change process. The management of technical change does not feature on most business and management courses. Where it does appear it is usually presented in relation to only one of the academic disciplines – economics, sociology or technology – and gives little guidance on what actions the manager should take.
- Although it is possible to sketch a scenario of the innovative firm, it is extremely difficult to formulate the path which the individual company should take to transform itself from its present position to the desired end point.

This book addresses these two problems. It looks at the totality of the problem and presents the main conclusions from the current knowledge of the technical change process in a form that it is hoped will be easily understood by practising managers in all areas of the business. This leads to a structured, but not over-formalised, approach to the management of technical change. The most important questions which must be considered are listed. The answers to these questions, however, depend upon the nature of the industry, the characteristics of the individual company and the aspirations of its management. There can be no universal prescriptions for success. Nevertheless, it is the belief of the authors that an understanding of the process of technical change, allied with a systematic approach to its management, is essential.

Technology in society and business

We tend to think of technology as a modern phenomenon. It is not. Technology, which is the ability to understand the characteristics of the physical world and apply them in the service of man, is the major trait that distinguishes us from other animals. Man's curiosity, inventiveness and desire for improvement have been present throughout history. It may be more formalised today, but its inherent motivation is unchanged.

There is, however, a conflicting force running through society. This is a fear of the unknown and the desire to reduce uncertainty. It manifests itself in institutions with well-established procedures to guide the actions of decision makers. They are based upon learning from what has worked well in the past. But institutions are conservative. Because they are rooted in the past they may become inappropriate to the conditions of the present. The assumptions on which they were based are never questioned. This inflexibility contains the seeds of their eventual decline as they fail to adapt to changes in their environment, for the environment is constantly changing. Eventually this position becomes untenable. Thus in history we see the demise of the great civilisations of the past or their transformation by revolution.

Business is a microcosm of society. It too contains the conflicting forces of change and innovation, which can lead to anarchy if left unbridled, and institutionalisation, which can result in ossification. Most large organisations have developed rigid procedures for their management which have served them well in periods of relative stability in their business environment. However, the changes in the business environment cannot be ignored. At the present time it is the advances in technology which are amongst the most significant factors in the environment to which businesses must be sensitive.

Many companies have suffered the fate of the great civilisations of the past. Few of the major firms of the 1950s remain amongst the leaders today. The remainder have gone out of business, declined, or suffered a revolution through take-over. One also notes that the newest technologies are to a large extent being exploited by new entrepreneurial ventures. Governments actively encourage the formation of these technology-based new enterprises. One could gain the impression that there is a widespread belief that the established businesses are incapable of change and that the future of an industrial society depends upon the emergence of new companies to replace them.

There is no inevitability about this. Whilst the success of the new ventures is based upon technical ability, creativity and entrepreneurship, they also have a high failure rate due to a lack of basic management expertise and inadequate financial resources. What the new ventures lack the established companies usually possess. However, if the large companies are to survive and prosper in the future they must integrate the technical expertise, innovativeness and entrepreneurship of the new ventures with their own strengths. It is a matter of striking the right corporate balance between these two conflicting basic human traits. This will be a constant theme throughout this book. Much can be learnt from those few successful companies which have managed to resolve this conflict.

Technology, management and change

All new technology inevitably changes an organisation to some extent. When its introduction is left entirely to the technologist these changes are likely to be unforeseen, unplanned and often disruptive. They may lead to opposition from those affected, which may limit substantially the benefits obtained compared with the initial expectations. However, it is by no means certain that the proposals made by the technologist are the most appropriate for the company. The contribution of technology is too important for corporate success to be left to the judgement of the technologist alone. The technological tail cannot be allowed to wag the corporate dog.

Yet it must also be recognised that it is the technologist who possesses the detailed knowledge. Only the technologist can assess many aspects of its potential. Nevertheless, his or her evaluation may not be carried out in relation to criteria which reflect the wider needs and capabilities of the business as a whole. The technologist may not appreciate the impact on marketing, manufacture, finance or personnel. This will certainly be the case if the technologist's corporate role is regarded as that of a specialist.

Examination of companies which have been most successful in exploiting technology shows that their most senior technologists are closely involved in the corporate strategic processes. But perhaps most importantly, the technologists themselves in these firms are capable of taking the wider business view. They have evolved from being technologists pure and simple into businesspeople. For the individual technologist this expansion of his or her role takes time and can occur only with the encouragement and involvement that top management alone can provide. This will not happen unless top management appreciates the strategic potential of technology and recognises the complexity of the innovation process.

The situation described above might appear to suggest that the stimulus for technical change should come from the technologist. Thus the managerial problem is to ensure that it meets with a favourable, though critical, reception. It will then be evaluated in relation to corporate needs and those organisational adjustments necessary to permit its speedy implementation are made. This process can be regarded as technology push. It is the normal approach to the adoption of the most radical advances and to the implementation of many smaller improvements. It is addressing the question: 'We have a technical potential; how best can we exploit it?'.

The role of technology can also be considered from a different viewpoint. This can be regarded as strategy pull. In this situation one is starting from the strategic objectives of the business, where the question is: 'How might technology contribute to meeting our strategic objectives?'. These will reflect the long-term aims of the organisation, where technology is only one of the resources upon which the company can draw. As will be seen later, the recent advances in technology make it the most important resource that many companies can use to maintain a competitive advantage. This reinforces the argument for a greater corporate role for technologists who have developed the capability to perform it.

The identification of how technology might best be harnessed to serve the business, important as it is, is only the starting point. It does not guarantee success. This depends upon the ability of the organisation to implement the decisions effectively. This is a management function. But good managers cannot ensure success in the absence of a corporate environment which enables them to mobilise and utilise all the resources required. Often this is lacking because the culture, the organisational structure, the skills and the attitudes have evolved to meet traditional needs with different requirements. An attempt to impose the new technology and working methods leads to resistance, which is likely to result in failure. Although it may sometimes be possible to modify the application of the technology to some extent to match the organisation as it is, this is generally unlikely to prove successful. The organisation itself must change in order to satisfy the imperatives of the change process.

It is, of course, easy to write about the need for cultural, organisational or attitudinal change. It is far more difficult to introduce them into a business where the status quo is embodied in individual managers at all levels. Furthermore, even where the need to change is accepted, change cannot be introduced quickly. A long-term view must be taken and the necessary changes introduced at a pace which is realistic in the light of what is possible. However, change will not occur without the identification by top management of what is required and management's commitment to the need to manage the changes in all aspects. There is a complex interaction between technology, management and change where attention must be focused upon the totality rather than individual aspects.

This introduction raises some of the most important issues addressed in this book. These will be explored in greater detail in the chapters which follow. In summary, it is based upon the recognition that technical change:

- affects all businesses;
- is of increasing strategic importance;
- almost invariably requires organisational change to be effective;
- is a process that must be actively managed;
- requires a corporate environment which encourages creativity and innovation at all levels;
- is a prime responsibility of top management;
- has an impact throughout the business, affecting all functions;
- must be planned and implemented with regard to the knowledge about the innovation process which is available.

'One of the ominous facts about growth and decay is that the present success of an organisation does not necessarily constitute grounds for optimism.'
John W. Gardner

1 The need for technical change

Why is it different today?

Technology affects all businesses. In manufacturing it is embodied in the products, in the physical processes by which they are made and, increasingly, in the managerial systems controlling all operations. In services the applications may appear to be more restricted, but can in reality demand an even more fundamental reappraisal of the nature of the service offered, the organisation, and the operational and managerial systems.

It might be argued that technology has been introduced into companies for many years without the attention it now receives. There have been both successes and failures. When these are examined it might seem that in most cases the distinguishing factor has been the operational competence of the managers involved. In recent years, however, there has been a growing realisation of the importance of the framework within which the technology is managed: the culture of the business, its strategies, the organisational structure and the managerial style. All these characteristics of the company must be tuned to the needs of technical change. Although this was important in the past it was still possible, even if less likely, to succeed in a corporate environment not designed specifically to support the needs of technical change. This is no longer the case.

For a number of reasons the contribution of technology as a source of competitive advantage is becoming of central importance in many businesses. But perhaps of greater concern to management is the rate of change, which adds to the complexity of decision making. Furthermore, the organisational response, the management of the technical change, must be rapid if the benefits are to be achieved before they are overtaken by further advances. Although technology affects all businesses, there are no universal prescriptions for its management. This will depend upon the nature of the industry, the individual company and the characteristics of its management. But before analysing how a company can match the technology to its own situation it is useful to review the developments which lead to the view that the corporate role of technical change is for most managements different today from what it has been in the past. These are the:

- rate of progress in many of the new technologies;
- limited potential of some of the long-established technologies;
- growth of technology-based new business ventures;
- increasing importance of product performance rather than price in many purchasing decisions;
- relationship of profitability with high added value;
- shortening product lives;
- escalation of the cost of technical development;
- increase in the number of technological competences needed within the firm.

The rate of technological advance

It is a common belief that the rate of technological advance is increasing. This, like most generalisations, is only partly true. On closer examination it is found that some technologies are advancing rapidly whilst others are slowing down. This is an important distinction to make, for although it is the management of those that are undergoing rapid progress that is the main concern of this book, they can be assessed only in the context of all the technologies a company is, or may be, involved with.

The most outstanding impact of technology in recent years is the phenomenal progress of microelectronics, manifesting itself in the growth of computational capability and in information technology (IT). This has affected all businesses and is the prime stimulus for change in service industry. Indeed, for many managers technical change is synonymous with information technology. In spite of the widespread application of these advances this revolution is still in its early days. For most companies the further developments into expert systems and artificial intelligence have yet to become a reality.

Few companies have managed to escape serious problems in their attempts to exploit what is currently available. Management has never before been faced with such a bewildering choice of alternatives or a technology which has maintained a high rate of advance for so long. Many systems have become outdated before they are fully installed and functioning properly. Yet the potential for improved corporate performance is so great that the problems cannot be avoided by waiting until the technology stabilises. The difficulties relate to both decision making – the type and scope of the application – and the management of its implementation. The scale of the financial investment is often substantial and for many organisations much greater than any previous allocation of resources to technology. However, it is in the management of the implementation process that the most serious problems are often experienced, and this will be a major concern of this book.

The immediacy and magnitude of the IT decisions, important as they are, should not blind management to the rapid progress in a number of other technologies which might be critical for the company's long-term survival. With the exception of manufacturers of electronic products, the main impact of IT is in reducing product cost through improved productivity and managerial efficiency, and in providing a better service. The development of entirely new products or significant improvements in current products may require the application of one or more of the other technologies which are advancing rapidly.

It is beyond the scope of this book to review the totality of advancing technology, although it is worth mentioning a few technologies briefly. Whilst none is likely to have as widespread an impact throughout industry as microelectronics, the application of one or a few of them may be more significant for a particular company by providing the ability to develop new or improved products. Biotechnology, for example, whilst still at a relatively early stage in its exploitation, provides many opportunities both for large companies with a competence in similar technologies and for new enterprises. Applications include agriculture, food and medicine, and it will have an impact in the service sector, for example in health care. Another area of rapid advance is in materials. Ceramics in particular are likely to have a major influence on the engineering industry at the expense of traditional materials. There is also a growth in the so-called science-based technologies, e.g. hybrid technologies such as protein engineering and superconductivity.

The implications for management are:

- Technologies which have not previously been of concern to a company must be identified and evaluated in relation to their strategic potential.
- The rate of advance may give little time for response if opportunities are to be seized or major threats averted.
- Decisions may have to be taken whilst major uncertainties remain, thus increasing the level of unavoidable business risk.
- Technology is becoming the key factor in the corporate environment for many businesses.

Technological maturity

No technology has unlimited potential. Eventually its advance will be constrained by a physical limit. This is analogous with the growth of a market which approaches saturation. In both cases the growth through

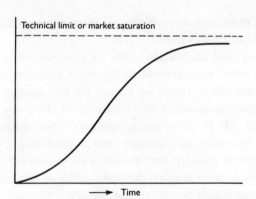

Fig. 1.1 The S-curve of technological progress

time follows an S-shaped curve (Fig. 1.1) When a technology or a market approaches the upper limit there is a much diminished scope for improvement in product performance or market size by either research and development (R&D) or marketing investment. An industry based on such a technology is approaching a stage of stability and maturity.

The stability of the mature industry is illusory. It may last for many years, but eventually it will be exposed to a threat from some new direction, often unforeseen. The longer the period of stability, the greater the likelihood of corporate complacency and consequently the greater its vulnerability when the threat emerges. More often than not it is technology which provides the foundation for that threat. The radical new technology-based industries may be the most glamorous, but the most frequent manifestation of new technology is its incorporation in products serving existing markets. Thus the musket replaced the bow and arrow, plastics replaced many metal products, synthetic materials replaced natural and, more recently, electronics replaced electromechanical products.

In assessing the effects of a new technology it is necessary to relate it to the unexploited potential of the old, that is, to look at where they are on the S-curve. When one examines the technological base of many of the largest companies it is apparent that for many of them the technologies which contributed to their past growth are close to the limit of their exploitable potential. Often this is insufficiently appreciated and the threat from the new technology is countered by an increased investment in the old, a policy which is doomed to failure. Even where the threat is understood at the strategic level there are severe difficulties in making the desired response due to the managerial attitudes developed during the period of stability.

At the time when the new technology emerges the mature company is likely to possess considerable strength in the markets it serves. However, examination of what has happened in the past suggests that market strength may be of little value, since success has usually been associated with technological strength. The electric light bulb was not exploited by the manufacturers of gas mantles, plastics by the metal industry, or the electronic watch by the Swiss watch industry. It may not be easy to build up an expertise in a new technology, but the necessity cannot be avoided if the market is not to be surrendered. Companies with products based on the new technology can succeed in markets where they have no previous experience.

The management literature suggests that these problems would not occur if companies addressed the question: 'What business are we in?'. This approach is appealing intellectually; it can assist in identifying strategic alternatives. Important as this is, there has been less attention paid to how the desired change can be translated into corporate action. As a consequence the process of technological substitution has frequently been accompanied by that of company substitution. The difficulties in achieving the changes should not be underestimated, but they are not insuperable. Some companies in the USA, Europe and particularly Japan have managed to sustain a continued process of technology-stimulated strategic change. These companies provide a model for the management of technical change throughout the business world.

It can be concluded that:

- The association of past success with a particular technology is not a guarantee for the future if that technology is approaching its limit of exploitable potential, i.e. if it is near the top of the S-curve.
- Technical expertise is likely to be more important than market strength in the exploitation of a new technology.
- The companies most vulnerable to technical change are those with the greatest financial and psychological commitment to the technologies on which their past growth has been based.

Technology-based new ventures

Many of the companies that have been most successful in exploiting the new technologies are of recent formation. Typically they have been founded by entrepreneurs with a technical background. In many cases these entrepreneurs have established their own enterprises after leaving large companies where they have failed to gain support for their ideas. Their success has been achieved in spite of weaknesses in many of the traditional areas of management such as marketing and financial control. The acquisition of finance is often a major problem for them. Nevertheless, in spite of a high failure rate, many have flourished. Their number is growing and their value to the economy is increasingly being recognised by financial institutions and encouraged by governments. Silicon Valley in the USA and the Cambridge Science Park in the UK are but two examples of this phenomenon where a concentration of new ventures is found.

Every successful new venture represents a lost opportunity by the large companies. Yet the established businesses possess, or can acquire, the technical knowledge, they usually have the financial resources, and they have the managerial skills which should enable them to achieve a higher success rate than the new ventures. There are, of course, large companies which have always been at the forefront of technological change. However, the history of technology is full of examples where innovations which have later transformed an industry have been rejected by its leaders. There are many reasons for these decisions, which may have seemed logical at the time but appear absurd in retrospect, e.g. the rejection of the telephone by Western Union in the USA. It must be recognised that the uncertainties are so great that there will always be a place for the individual entrepreneur. Nevertheless, the emergence of so many new ventures for the exploitation of the advancing technologies today indicates a challenge that cannot be ignored by the established companies. The alternative is to surrender a high proportion of the profitable innovations of the future to newcomers.

The managerial differences between the two types of company will be discussed in more detail later. At this stage it can be seen that the main implications for established companies are:

- The growth in the number of new technology-based companies represents a challenge they cannot afford to ignore.
- Their financial, marketing and managerial strengths ought to enable them to apply new technology more successfully than the new enterprises.
- They need to explore the factors which make for success in technological innovation, identify their own shortcomings and develop a managerial culture, attitudes and organisation which combine their own strengths with the needs of technical change.

Product performance v. product price

There are a number of features a prospective customer takes into account when making a purchasing decision. These include performance, quality, reliability, after-sales service and aesthetic appeal as well as price. The customer has a choice involving trade-offs between these attributes based on the weight he or she attaches to each in his or her mind. These weightings are unlikely to be examined explicitly; nevertheless, they exist in the customer's subconscious evaluation of the product. It should also be noted that some of them are difficult to assess in quantitative terms.

In the developed world there have been two trends which affect the circumstances in which the purchasing decision is made. First, the choice of products has widened, partly due to the expansion of international markets and partly because of the more extended product range offered by each manufacturer. Thus it is possible for customers to find products which meet their requirements more closely. Secondly, increasing affluence has reduced the importance of price relative to other factors in the buying decision. As a consequence customers can afford, and are willing, to pay more for the products which match their needs most closely.

Price will always remain an important factor. In some industries economic factors are critical. For example in the purchase of civil aircraft the aircraft price, its operating cost and the financing package available are the major concerns. In contrast to this is the low market penetration of Eastern European motorcars in Western markets, which indicates that the low price is inadequate compensation for their lack of technical sophistication. Price remains the major factor, however, in choosing between products which are broadly similar in all other respects.

Technology contributes to both product performance and cost reduction. Few companies can avoid investing in both these areas, but with limited resources a choice must be made about the relative scale of the investment to be made in product development compared with manufacturing processes. A feature of many companies faced with increasing competition is the channelling of more funds into cost reduction at the expense of developing new products. It will be seen later that this is unlikely to yield the desired results in the long term when competitors are focusing on the development of new products to meet the needs of a less cost-conscious market. Thus in many industries competitive advantage is increasingly being derived by harnessing technology to develop new products or enhance the performance of existing products rather than to reduce cost.

Because of the effects of this evolving market it is necessary for a business to consider:

- the importance of product price in achieving a competitive advantage;
- the trend in consumer preference in its industry;
- whether it is necessary to enlarge its product range in order to satisfy an increase in the segmentation of its market;
- the implications of the above for investment in both product development and cost-reducing manufacturing processes.

Profitability and added value

A feature of the trends discussed in the previous section is the increasing degree of market segmentation. At the bottom end of the market are the mass products sold largely on the basis of price but themselves undergoing a continual growth in technical sophistication. Above this level are an expanding number of smaller segments aimed at meeting the needs of more selective customers.

Success in the mass market is associated with either cheap labour, if the product is labour intensive, or manufacturing competence, if it is capital intensive. In the former case it is clear that the relatively high wage rates in the USA and Europe impose an almost insuperable obstacle. In the latter case there are no inherent reasons why companies in the developed world cannot compete successfully, as indeed a number do, although in a number of industries Japan has established a dominant position. However, in either case the market is highly competitive, with low profit margins. Market success is often accompanied by a low return on investment.

Examination of the most profitable companies indicates that they are often to be found at the high-added-value end of the market catering for the more specialised segments, where price is less important. Some companies, appreciating this, have undertaken significant changes in their strategic emphasis. ICI, for example, has moved its focus away from bulk chemicals, where margins are low, to pharmaceuticals and speciality chemicals, where they are high. In the motor industry Mercedes and Porsche have been more profitable than Renault, Rover or the European subsidiaries of Ford and G.M. Within the product range the most profitable models are frequently those that feature technological innovations such as four-wheel drive or anti-locking brake systems. In most of these examples the higher added value has been achieved through technical advances.

In general it can be concluded that:

- Profitability is closely related to high added value.
- Technology provides the basis for adding value.

Shortening product lives

The life of a product is to a large extent dependent upon the rate of advance in the technology on which it is based. Where the technology is advancing rapidly the period for which a product can be marketed profitably is much shorter than with a mature technology. This can be seen today in a number of industries. For example, in the sound-recording industry, the gramophone record was the standard for half a century, with minor innovations such as the replacement of the metal needle by the fibre-tipped and then the diamond stylus and the development of the LP and EP records. At decreasing intervals the vinyl record has been largely replaced by the tape, then the compact disc and later the digital audio tape, of unknown market potential at the time of writing.

Although product lives have been shortening in many industries, it must not be assumed that this is universally true. The rate of technological progress is not the only factor to be taken into account. In aerospace, for example, the high development and capital costs of new civil aircraft have meant that financial factors have restricted the pace of fleet replacement; thus the Boeing 747 and the RB–211 aero engine have had considerably longer lives than their equivalents in the 1950s and 1960s. In pharmaceuticals, the development cost and time are slowing the rate of introduction of new drugs, largely as a consequence of legislation to make clinical testing more stringent due to public concern regarding product safety. Thus in assessing the product life trend in a particular industry it is necessary to take into account the impact of all the environmental influences – social, political, legal and economic as well as technological.

The main implications for industries where product lives are reducing are:

- the increased frequency of new product introductions;
- the need to reduce product development times in order to enable an early market launch (a six-month development delay is much more serious when the expected market life is three years than when it is ten years);
- the importance of 'getting it right first time', since there is little opportunity to modify a faulty design or regain market share lost through customer disenchantment caused by the problems experienced with early models.

In general these conditions cannot be achieved without an increase in the financial resources allocated to product development and an emphasis on the quality of project management.

Escalating product development costs

In many industries the cost of developing new products has risen sharply in recent years. The effect upon the aerospace and pharmaceutical industries has been mentioned in the previous section. When this is combined with a possible reduction in product life, companies, even the largest in an industry, face a dilemma. If they fail to innovate they can expect a competitive decline; if they attempt to innovate they may be unable to finance the developments or to recover the investment through a relatively small sales volume during a limited life. This problem will extend to a wider range of industries in the years ahead.

One of the consequences of this trend can be observed in the domination of such industries by one or a few large companies, often multinationals. A logical response by other companies in the industry might be to seek a take-over or merger with one of the leaders before it is too late or to diversify into other activities where the conditions are more favourable. There are, however, other alternatives for a business which wishes to remain independent. These include:

- a concentration of effort on a narrower base by exploiting a technical strength by –
  (a) developing an excellence in only one part or a few parts of the total system, e.g. loudspeakers or amplifiers rather than radio or TV systems
  (b) seeking niche markets where a large market share of a relatively small market can be captured, particularly if the added value is high, e.g. scientific computers;
- forming an alliance with a similar company in order to share either market or development costs, or both.

These trends in the cost of product development cannot be ignored. In many cases they can be countered only by a major re-alignment of the corporate strategy. Although there are a number of alternatives that can be explored, it is evident that only the very largest companies will be in a position to maintain their traditional range of activities unchanged.

Expansion of the technological base

A common effect of developments in technology is to blur the traditional distinctions between industries. For example, a large chemical company today is likely to be involved in food, textiles and pharmaceuticals as well as bulk and speciality chemicals. It is applying its technology to a range of applications in a number of different markets, both consumer and industrial. But it is unlikely to possess resources or expertise in all these markets. Thus in some situations it may be necessary to form joint ventures or to take over a company with the market knowledge in order to exploit its technological strength. One example is Marlow Foods, where a chemical company (ICI) formed a joint venture with a food company (RHM) to utilise its capability in biotechnology in a market where it had no experience.

At the same time the products are themselves incorporating a larger number of technologies. The most dramatic example is provided by microelectronics, which is finding applications in the products of most industries, for example in engine management systems in the motor industry. But the electronic industry itself is becoming increasingly dependent upon materials technology, as in the development of integrated circuits and superconductors.

Market / Technology	1	2	3
A	●	●	●

(a) Traditional business: core technology (A) in products for markets 1, 2 and 3

Market / Technology	1	2	3
A	●	●	●
B		●	●
C	●		●

(b) Traditional business: need for additional technologies (B and C) to produce products acceptable to developed markets

Company Y

Market / Technology	1	2	3	3A	4
A	●	●	●	●	●
B		●	●		●
C				●	●
D				●	

Company X

(c) Business expansion by either:
 ● developing new products for market 3 (3A) using new technology (D) possessed by company X; or
 ● developing new market (4) using own technologies in conjunction with company Y, which possesses experience in marketing

Fig. 1.2 Market/technology business configurations: evolution to complexity

Thus we see that the simple identification of an industry or company with one technology and one market or a limited number of markets is being transformed into a complex matrix of alternatives (Fig. 1.2). Strategic choices have to be made. Survival in the traditional product-market is dependent upon embracing contributions from other technologies. At the same time, growth may be achieved by employing this technological breadth in new markets. Most firms, however, do not possess the resources, either in finance or in competence, to expand both their technical and their market bases. Thus they may find it desirable to seek partners who can provide the expertise they lack. One example of this is the joint venture, Living Technology, between Pilkington and BOC to develop and market medical lasers. For this reason one sees a reduction in self-sufficiency and a growth of mergers, joint ventures and technical or marketing agreements crossing the traditional demarcations. The alternative is to reduce the scope of the business by focusing on specialist technical applications or niche markets.

These trends have a number of implications:

- *Strategic.* The company must consider the needs for technical or market diversification and how they can be satisfied in isolation or in conjunction with other companies.
- *Technical.* It is necessary to identify, evaluate and acquire the additional technologies needed for developing new products.
- *Financial.* It is unlikely that the technical base can be expanded without additional investment in technology, although the size of this investment may be reduced through some form of joint venture.
- *Managerial.* The dominant position and status of the company's core technology within the technical department may inhibit the recruitment of high-calibre staff in the newer technologies; this is reflected in the poor mechanical design found in many electronic products and the low reliability of the electronics incorporated in many mechanical engineering products.

Summary

A number of trends in the business role of technology have been considered. In general it can be concluded that, taken together, their impact on business is that technical change:

(a) is an essential consideration for all companies, including those for which it has been of little relevance in the past;
(b) is likely to be the key factor in the business environment;
(c) is becoming a, if not the, prime source of competitive advantage;

(d) has a strategic impact which may necessitate significant changes in the structure of the market and industry; thus it must be a major concern of top management;

(e) is likely to require a higher level of investment in product development and manufacturing processes than in the past;

(f) affects all parts of the business, demanding a high degree of functional integration;

(g) requires a culture, managerial style and organisational structure that are different from those appropriate in a stable, mature business; thus the successful introduction of technical change cannot be divorced from managerial change.

Having set the scene, it is now necessary to establish guidelines whereby it is possible to assess how these influences affect a particular industry and then analyse the position of the individual company within that industry. To some extent that must be an iterative process, since it has been seen already that one of the effects of technology may be to cause a redefinition of the industry itself. It has also been observed that where a technology is evolving rapidly it, rather than market strength, is more likely to be the determinant of commercial success. Many companies which identify with their market rather than their technology must question whether this orientation will still be appropriate in the future.

Assessing changes in the technical environment of an industry

A company needs to change because the environment in which it is trading is changing. If this were not so, business success would be associated wholly with the effectiveness of its internal operations: *how* it does it. Since the external environment is not static, its implications must be studied and the company's strategy modified accordingly: *what* it does.

At a time of rapid technological change the impression might be gained that analysis of current trends in the technology itself provides an adequate basis for decision making. This is not so. Decisions taken now come to fruition at some time in the future. They must be proactive, anticipating the conditions when they take effect, rather than reactive, responding to changes that have already occurred elsewhere. Whilst it must be recognised that opportunism may yield substantial short-term profits and cannot be ignored, it is unlikely to ensure long-term profitability for an organisation unless it can be reconciled with the strategic objectives.

Technology is only one of the influences on the business environment, although for many companies it may be the most important. However,

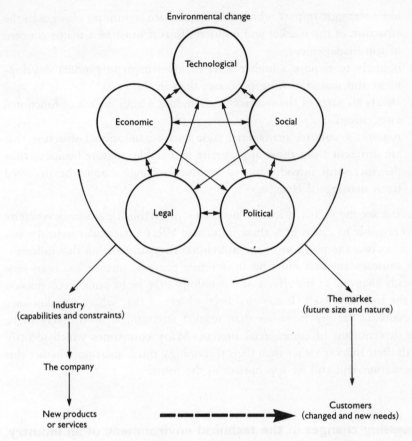

Fig. 1.3 Environmental trends and their impact on both industry and the market

it can be assessed only in relation to economic, social, legal and political factors with which it interacts in a complex set of relationships (Fig. 1.3). All of these undergo change and it is necessary to consider how each is evolving and how they interact in order to understand the forces shaping the future environment of the business. These same forces are also influencing the future needs of customers. Thus the analysis of these trends must extend to an understanding of their impact on the market, with the aim of matching the future capabilities of the company to the future demands not only of today's customers but also of potential new customers.

We must now turn to technology and the forces which lead to progress. In doing so it is important to draw a clear distinction between science and technology. Scientific advances, the extension of human knowledge, are the consequence of human curiosity and a search for an understanding of the nature of the physical world. In the past this has normally been conducted without any concern for its practical application, although this is no longer wholly true. Technology, however, is the application of scientific knowledge to serve the needs of society or individuals. It does not advance of its own accord: it requires a financial investment which will not be forthcoming unless those sanctioning it believe the result will contribute to the achievement of their objectives, which, for commercial concerns, will be financial. The leads directly to the marketplace. If a potential technological advance is unlikely to satisfy a market need then one would not expect the funds to be made available to translate the potential into reality.

With the benefit of hindsight it can be seen that technological progress beyond the early stages has always been associated with a market demand. The problem is that it is far from easy to assess what the future market needs might be for an emerging technology. Often the major market has proven to be quite different from that for which the first applications were developed. This is one of the reasons why so many of the technical break-throughs, e.g. xerography, have resulted from the commitment of dedi-cated technologists in the face of universal rejection by leading companies. With perfect knowledge of the future it would be possible to apply rigorous evaluation procedures before initiating technical development. Without that knowledge these same procedures are likely to result in the rejection of all but the most minor innovations. This is a dilemma to which there are no simple answers. Uncertainty cannot be divorced from risk. However, if an organisation is to prosper it must attempt to minimise risk, though not to such an extent that it eschews the challenge of change. In the longer term the risks from doing nothing are likely to be much higher than those associated with introducing technical change.

It might be thought that the implied emphasis placed on the long term in this section is not particularly relevant to applications of new tech-nology in management and manufacturing systems. There is some validity in this, but with the trend towards greater capital intensity in these areas, decisions have to be taken with a longer-term perspective than in the past; in spite of the flexibility in the design of many of these systems it must remain the aim to obtain the maximum working life from any investment. All too often one finds cases where investments are made in order to match current best practice rather than with an eye on the future, resulting in their obsolescence by the time they are installed. But one also finds examples where over-ambitious changes have been accompanied by failure to achieve in practice the anticipated targets.

The adoption of new technology is often done on an ad hoc basis without due consideration of the most appropriate form and the timing of its introduction. But before addressing the *what* and the *when* for a company it is necessary to establish, in so far as is possible, what is happening in its technological environment. The time dimension of technical progress must be assessed. In this section we shall explore how the uncertainties of change can be reduced by analysis and understanding of the patterns of technological progress. Although trends in economic, social and political forces will not be explored in detail, their importance in the development of both technological capability and the market must not be ignored.

The most important questions to be addressed are:

- *What is the appropriate time scale for an analysis of the future?* Much evidence exists to suggest that many companies emphasise short-term financial performance rather than long-term trends of strategic importance. In deciding the time frame to be considered in a particular industry two factors must be considered:

  (a) the rate of technological progress;

  (b) the flexibility and the lead times to respond to change.

  The latter is determined by the nature of the investment decisions. A major investment in specialised equipment, for example an ethylene plant, may need a time frame of 20 years or more, whereas a few years may be adequate for general-purpose machine tools.

- *What are the significant trends in the environment of the industry within this time scale?* This requires the identification of technological, economic, social and political factors and how they interact.

- *How can we evaluate these trends?* This is the most difficult part of the exercise, since it involves the assessment of time scales. It is much easier to identify *what* might happen in the future than to assess the *time* of occurrence. There are many forecasting techniques to assist in this, but they are not widely known or used. For most purposes, however, accurate forecasts are not necessary. Examination of major corporate failures shows that they more often resulted from ignoring strong signals rather than from inaccuracies in forecasts of their timing.

- *What are the likely consequences of these trends?* This must be considered in relation to:

  (a) the structure of the industry;

  (b) the capabilities of the industry;

  (c) the nature of the market;

  (d) the needs of individual customers.

- *What should our company do?* This is the key question, and will be examined later. It should not, however, be considered until the previous questions have been answered adequately.

Technical progress does not occur in a random fashion. There are identifiable patterns which provide strong clues to the future performance levels of a technology and their timing. They cannot, of course, provide accurate forecasts, but they can give a picture of the dynamics of development. All too often in the authors' experience important technical investments are made in relation to the conditions at the time they are made – a snapshot – rather than in relation to the evolving pattern – a film. Few managements are aware of these patterns which give a valuable input to decision making for technical change. The most important of these will now be described briefly.

The technology life cycle

The S-shaped technology life cycle (Fig. 1.1) represents the typical path of technological progress. In theory the technical performance (y-axis) should be plotted against the cumulative investment (x-axis) which causes it. Usually investment data are not available, so time is plotted on the x-axis. For most business decisions this presents no problems provided cognisance is taken of any reasons why investment might be curtailed, thereby halting progress. It is worth repeating that technology is market driven through the medium of finance.

At any point in time it is possible to plot the progress of the technology to date. Sometimes accurate data may not be available but this is unlikely to be a critical problem, since the decision maker is concerned primarily with the general shape of the curve rather than with obtaining an accurate forecast. The other information required is the upper limit of the curve. This may be determined by a natural physical limit, in the case of a technical performance parameter, or by a saturation level for a market parameter. This can raise problems initially, since a surprising number of technologists do not consider explicitly how they should measure their technologies and their limits. This is inexcusable and general managers should insist on obtaining from them answers to the following questions:

- How do you measure the performance of the technologies with which you are working?
- What is the theoretical maximum performance obtainable from these technologies?
- How near is current performance to this limit?

A market saturation level cannot be derived with the same degree of precision. There are forecasts available for many industries, but in others management must make its own judgements. It is advisable to do this on both an optimistic and a pessimistic basis. However, in a number of cases the author has examined, it has been found that a wide divergence between the two levels is necessary before there is a major impact on the business decision. Once the portion of the S-curve to date and the limiting level have been established it is possible to draw the remainder of the curve, namely the expected future progress.

Examination of the curve shows that it can be conveniently considered as consisting of three stages, discussed below.

Stage 1: early development

This is the flat portion at the bottom of the curve. It represents the early period of the technology before it has found a major market application. It is characterised by:

- a low rate of growth, often associated with a high degree of technical optimism;
- a high level of investment to obtain marginal improvements in performance due to major technical uncertainties;
- practical applications in specialist uses where it is competing in fields where earlier technologies are inadequate, e.g. defence;
- an underestimation of the period before it reaches the point of rapid growth; this peiod may extend for several decades, e.g. carbon fibres and robotics, considered imminent in the 1950s.

Investment in technologies at this stage of development must be viewed critically and any optimism tempered with caution. For most companies the future potential should be noted and progress monitored, but little action taken. Others may feel it desirable to build up an expertise so that they can respond rapidly when the curve turns up sharply with the onset of Stage 2.

Stage 2: rapid growth

The centre portion of the curve exhibits the main period of the exploitation of the technology. In the early part of this stage growth is extremely rapid, which, following the slow progress made in Stage 1, may lead to an underestimate of its significance. The early part of this stage is characterised by:

- a rapid succession of new products each of significantly higher performance than its predecessor;
- short product lives before technical obsolescence;
- the need for short development times rather than cost minimisation to ensure competitive advantage;

- a proliferation of different approaches to the application of the technology;
- business success closely identified with a technical orientation, expertise and strong R&D;
- the emergence of new venture companies.

In the latter part of this stage the major technical uncertainties have been resolved, with the result that:

- A dominant design configuration will have emerged, although within it there is still scope for technology-based product differentiation.
- Whilst the total market continues to grow, there is a greater emphasis on market segmentation and products designed to meet the needs of individual segments.
- Product lives lengthen.
- Product cost becomes more important.

Stage 3: the approach of maturity

The rapid growth during Stage 2 frequently leads to business complacency. Success achieved during the period of rapid growth can engender a feeling that the good days will last for ever. Market growth may have led to increased profits which distract attention from shrinking margins and loss of market share. Often there is major investment in new manufacturing throughout the industry at this stage, leading to overcapacity, increased competition and a pressure on margins. The main characteristics of this stage are:

- little scope for the introduction of radical new products;
- competition on price, with reduced margins;
- increased competition for share in a saturated market;
- the need to reduce costs, with technology focused on manufacturing processes;
- industrial concentration, with the emergence of a few dominant companies;
- an emphasis on quality often manifesting itself in the design of products with a longer in-service life; this can reduce the total size of the market, which is highly dependent upon the replacement market as saturation approaches;
- a high financial investment to obtain marginal improvements in technical performance.

Technological substitution

The technology life cycle described above relates to the progress of a particular technology measured by a parameter of performance. The limiting level relates to that technology. Another technology may have a higher limit for the same measure. Thus, for example, the speed of operation of many products incorporating mechanical components is limited by inertia, but this limitation is removed with the introduction of electronics, and thus a new S-curve is born (Fig. 1.4).

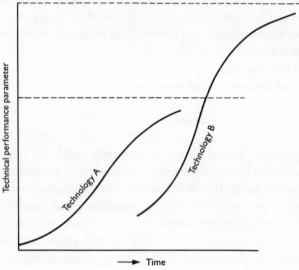

Fig. 1.4 Technological substitution

One might assume that the emergence of the new technology would result in a transfer of resources to it by companies previously reliant on the old technology. Frequently this does not happen. The most powerful reason for this is that the companies do not want it to happen: they are familiar with the old technology, they have investments locked into assets which cannot be used for the new technology and, most importantly in the context of this book, it involves changes, which they resist. A good example is provided by RCA, which was the leader in thermionic valves at the time of the advent of transistors. It recognised the potential of transistors, but made their development the responsibility of the department responsible for valve development. Successful transistors would make obsolete their major valve-manufacturing facilities. Thus, although in this case the potential of the new technology was recognised, the inertia provided by managerial attitudes and physical assets ensured that the company never achieved the leadership it had hitherto enjoyed in valves.

There are, however, a number of arguments that can be advanced to support this reluctance to move to the new technology, namely:

- the performance of the new technology at the base of the S-curve, which may be lower than that currently obtainable from the old technology;
- the slow progress exhibited by it in Stage 1;
- initial high costs where learning-curve benefits have yet to be achieved;
- the initial high unreliability of new technology;
- past experience of new technologies which never met their early high expectations.

These arguments have some validity. It is not advocated that a new technology should be adopted just because it is there. However, an appreciation and study of the S-curves of technological substitution can be a valuable help in assessing the impact of a new technology on an industry and in making a judgement on the time when action becomes necessary. Ignorance of this and a reluctance to take action are the major reasons why many leading companies have lost their markets to new venture companies or competitors which have espoused the new technology.

The emergence of new technology does not imply that the old should be abandoned prematurely. There may still be scope for improvement. In many office systems a re-evaluation of manual operations may delay the time when computerisation becomes appropriate. In manufacturing the existence of specialist equipment, a sunk cost, may make it feasible to reduce prices to delay the introduction of the new technology. But if the new technology has the capability to be substituted economically for the old, such actions are merely palliatives. They may delay the day of reckoning but cannot avert it. The timing of the change is the key managerial consideration.

Product substitution

Whilst consideration of the technology life cycle and technological substitution gives an essential understanding of the underlying forces at work in an industry, management is more directly concerned with assessing the rate of diffusion into the market of products incorporating the new technology.

This is extremely difficult to do when it first appears. However, this is of importance to only a relatively few companies, those which are striving for technical leadership. Most businesses are more concerned with the rate of substitution once the new technology has established itself by capturing a small proportion of the market. Examination of a large

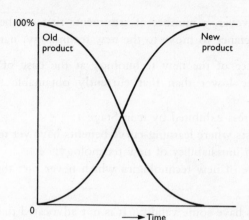

(a)   Market share: old product decay, new product growth

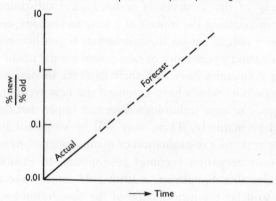

(b)   Ratio of new: old on log linear graph paper

Fig. 1.5 Product substitution

number of substitutions reveals that once again an S-shaped pattern is followed when the percentage substitution is plotted against time (Fig. 1.5(a)). This lends itself to a simple forecasting technique, since a straight line is obtained when the ratio of the new to the old is plotted on log-linear graph paper; extrapolation of this line enables future levels to be derived (Fig. 1.5(b)).

This valuable technique is not widely used in industry. The author has applied it to a number of substitutions which he has then monitored to see what actually happened for more than ten years. There include: radial for cross-ply tyres, diesel-engined motorcar for petrol, and colour for monochrome TV. In all cases the actual outcome was close to that forecast and frequently the forecast was significantly closer than the figures upon which the industry had based its investment.

There are, however, dangers in applying forecasting techniques mechanistically without an understanding of the underlying influences at work. Unexpected changes in the environment can affect the rate of substitution. The oil price rise in the 1970s influenced the rate of several substitutions, often with counter-intuitive results; for example it had a greater impact on the diffusion of colour TV than on car ownership.

It is recommended that the following procedure be adopted:

(a) Collect data for the diffusion of the new product to date.
(b) Plot and forecast to the company's planning horizon.
(c) Question what factors might modify the forecast. These may be economic, social, political, legal or environmental.
(d) Assess how each of these might affect the forecast. This must usually be a subjective exercise reflecting the consensus of managerial judgement. It will also indicate areas where more information is needed or trends which should be monitored.

It can be seen that this approach combines the results of a forecast with an informed managerial debate about all the factors which might modify it. There can, of course, be no guarantee that the final result will be borne out in actuality. However, this systematic analysis ensures that all relevant factors have been examined explicitly to the best of management's ability. This is the best that can be hoped for. It should be noted that this analysis leads to an assessment of the total market. It cannot indicate the market share for an individual company, since this depends upon that company's managerial decisions.

Attribute substitution

It was noted earlier that every product possesses a number of attributes. Their relative importance changes over time for a variety of reasons. The lower emphasis placed on product price in a number of developed markets has already been discussed. There are, however, other aspects which must be examined.

Technology contributes to a number of the attributes of a product. It must be focused on those attributes the market deems to be important. When the attribute values change so must the technological focus. There are several reasons for this, and these are discussed below.

Technical adequacy

There is a level of performance which satisfies completely the needs of the customer. In the 1970s body corrosion was a major concern in the motor industry and technology was applied to reducing it. That problem is now largely resolved, and it is unlikely that a purchaser is interested in a corrosion-free life of more than about 15 years. However, technical departments have an internal momentum which can easily lead to continued development beyond what the market requires. Similarly, with domestic disinfectants users are confident that an acceptable microbial kill rate is achieved by all the products on the market; it is in any case difficult for them to verify the manufacturers' claims. Once this level is achieved, other attributes, such as odour and colour, become more important.

It might also be desirable to change the emphasis of the technological effort before this stage is reached, when the traditional technology is approaching its limit and the technology contributing to another attribute is in an earlier stage of development. For a given expenditure a greater increment of performance can be obtained from the latter, leading to an enhancement of the overall desirability of the product.

Ideally these re-orientations should be appreciated within the technical department. But this may well not happen, and the stimulus must come from outside, from marketing or general management.

Environmental factors

Discontinuities in the business environment can create a change in customer priorities. The rapid escalation of energy costs in the 1970s increased the importance of fuel economy in many purchasing decisions. This in turn provided a stimulus to sophisticated electronics-based engine management systems in the motor industry. Whilst these developments would undoubtedly have occurred, the additional incentive brought forward their introduction. The company which can quickly translate these environmental changes into technical developments gains a competitive edge.

Fashion

This may not be an important factor for most technically based industries, but it should not be ignored in the wider business perspective. For example, severe over-capacity occurred in the hand-knitting wool industry when the fashion changed from chunky knitwear to finer designs not suitable for the hand-knitter. In such industries flexibility is essential and can be an important consideration in the choice of manufacturing processes.

Combination technologies

Many products are dependent upon contributions from several technologies which may be on different positions on the S-curve, frequently termed technological trajectories. Sometimes a desirable product may not be achievable because one of its technical constituents has not reached a sufficiently advanced state. The classic case is the jet engine, which was not economically feasible until high-temperature metals for turbine blades became available. Similarly, the accurate long-range missile was dependent upon compact electronics, the transistor and inertial guidance. Today microelectronics enables the potential of many other technologies to be fully exploited.

Usually the enabling technology will be in Stage 1 when the potential benefit of combining it with a more highly developed technology is first recognised. For many years it may languish in this stage, but once it enters Stage 2 the rate of increase in its performance can lead to the rapid diffusion of products combining the two. It is the speed at which this can occur that creates both opportunities and threats to businesses. It is essential, therefore, that progress is closely monitored, even though immediate action is unwarranted, so that a prompt response can be made when necessary.

System constraints

Many products are part of a larger technical or market system. Infrastructure requirements are particularly important. The early diffusion of the diesel car was dependent upon the provision of diesel fuel pumps on garage forecourts; the market for satellite TV receivers is limited by the provision of programmes. In general enthusiasts for the system seriously under-estimate the time scale for the provision of the infrastructure on which it depends.

Conclusion

In this introductory chapter we noted a number of trends which not only enhance the importance of technology in business but also have a major strategic impact. We then proceeded to explore how management can assess these trends and interpret them in the context of a specific industry.

At first sight the concepts described may appear to involve specialist techniques outside the concern of senior management. However, their importance is such that they cannot be left to technologists, many of whom are not accustomed to taking a corporate view of technology. This view often demands an assessment of factors outside their area of competence. The concepts themselves are not difficult to comprehend, although the application of the techniques to give more precise information must be left to specialists trained in them. We have also noted that some of the most useful approaches are not widely used.

We would contend that general management must be sufficiently familiar with these concepts in order to ask the appropriate questions. The answers are unlikely to be unambiguous, but they do provide a framework for systematic decision making. They introduce the time dimension, which enables the patterns of progress to be identified, thereby assisting the adoption of a proactive stance.

In the discussion a number of managerial implications have been briefly touched upon; these will be explored later in greater detail in relation to decision making in the individual firm. The process can be thought of in three stages:

(a) What is happening in the industrial and technical environment of our business?
(b) What changes are appropriate for our company?
(c) How do we implement the changes?

This chapter has addressed the first of these questions, an essential first stage leading on to the third, which is the main thrust of this book. But technical change demands organisational change. In the next chapter attention is directed to the nature of organisational change. This involves the culture of the company and the attitudes of its management. Change does not come easily; it takes time. For this reason, as well as because of the time it takes to develop an expertise in a new technology, it is imperative that a long-term view is taken.

2 The innovative organisation

This chapter looks at the nature of organisations and the degree to which organisational structure and behaviour present barriers or opportunities to the organisation's collective ability to regenerate itself through the application of technology. Many aspects of organisations retard and restrict change, but through the development of different organisational cultures and a high awareness of some of these barriers, companies are finding that they do have within them a high capacity for change and renewal.

We have to ask what an organisation is, other than a collection of individuals, because if it is just this then it is changing individuals on which we must concentrate. We believe that individuals are a major part of an organisation, but that an organisation is more than a random collection of people. Ideally, the people in an organisation are bound by a common purpose, though as we shall see this may not be the case, individuals often being bound merely by a series of structures and procedures. Organisations require individuals to conform to a wide range of rules, some formally laid down, but mostly in the form of 'that is the way we do things around here', even if we see them as being patently ridiculous. So it is at both the individual and the organisational level that we must examine whether and how we change.

The innovative organisation needs to behave in many ways like the small entrepreneurial venture company, yet take full advantage of the benefits of size and large resources. Innovation is a combination of the right individuals interacting with a challenging but supportive organisation. In this chapter we examine the relationship between the two and look at ways in which organisations and individuals can change to support technological change.

Example

When we were working in a public utility which was keen to introduce the latest technology and formed a top management committee to be in control, the rules were that the general managers could authorise capital expenditure up to £50 000 as long as it was not 'new technology'; this required the committee's approval even if it was for only £100. The general managers soon found that their ability to progress was stifled by the well-meaning committee's rules. The net result was that the hurdles were too high for those with initiative and ideas. The desire to introduce advanced technology was restricted by a well-intentioned but over-controlling and unsupportive management culture.

The traditional organisation and innovation

The traditional organisational structure was designed to approach perfect administrative efficiency. Max Weber,[1] in his classic essays on bureaucracy, laid down some of its basic characteristics:

(a) The regular activities required for the discharge of the bureaucratically governed structure are distributed in a fixed way as official duties.

(b) The principles of office hierarchy and of levels of graded authority mean a firmly ordered system of super- and subordination in which there is a supervision of the lower offices by the higher ones.

(c) The management of the office follows general rules, which are more or less stable, more or less exhaustive, and which can be learnt.

(d) Whether in a private office or a public bureau, the modern official always strives for and usually enjoys a distinct social esteem as compared with the governed.

(e) The decisive reason for the advance of bureaucratic organisation has always been its purely technical superiority over any other form of organisation. The fully developed bureaucratic mechanism compares with other organisations exactly as the machine with the non-mechanical forms of production.

(f) Precision, speed, unambiguity, knowledge of the files, continuity, discretion, unity, strict subordination, reduction of friction and of material and personal costs: these are raised to the optimum point in the strictly bureaucratic organisation.

We can place these six characteristics in the language of many of today's organisations:

(a) Fixed official duties = Detailed job description.

(b) Office hierarchy = Rigid organisational structure.

(c) General rules = Policies, procedures, the received wisdom as to how we do things in this organisation.

(d) Social esteem = Status gradations which reflect authority position, such as cars, offices, etc.

(e) The technical superiority of the organisation = Managerial control, the need for precise order to ensure everyone is doing what we want them to do according to our own prescription.

(f) Precision and speed = We believe that efficiency is the same as effectiveness and that the reduction of tension and conflict is beneficial to the smooth running of the organisation.

The business whose product is mature and declining has no guarantee of its survival and future effectiveness, however high its efficiency. We need a balance between ensuring that the production of our current products or services is efficiently carried out and preparing for new products and markets. The danger of having a concern only for efficiency is that it is such a short-term measure if taken on its own; 'effectiveness' suggests efficiency over a long period of time plus success in the marketplace.

Example

Efficiency and effectiveness. The *efficient* taxi driver is the one who drives you to your destination in a manner that maximises the car's fuel consumption; the *effective* taxi driver is the one who gets you there on time.

The underlying assumptions that Weber made still apply to many of our organisations. The first is that the world, and in particular our economic system, is more or less stable. Progress is seen to be gradual and not subject to major discontinuities. Furthermore, complex tasks are seen to be most efficiently executed through their subdivision into understandable elemental tasks. Frederick Taylor, the so-called father of scientific management, developed this concept from that of the pure bureaucracy to the manufacturing environment of the early twentieth century. The organisation of the work must be strictly separated from the actual doing of the work (management is a separate activity from doing). Then each activity is broken down into its elemental tasks which can be undertaken, without much thought and with great rapidity, by largely unskilled labour, spurred on by a promised pot of gold (the piecework method of payment) which precisely reflects the effort expended.

Neither Weber nor Taylor got to grips with the way in which organisations should change. They both believed that their ideas of the perfect organisational system applied universally irrespective of the nature of the product or service. Change for them was a transfer from one stable state to another, though neither had much to say about how such a transformation should take place.

The second major assumption that both theorists made was that organisational tasks and operations are complex but totally understandable. In Taylor's model that meant that the management had a monopoly of wisdom about the productive process and that slavish allegiance to their prescription was all that was required to achieve the highest productivity. The management systems of control are specifically designed to ensure the highest degree of conformity.

So although they both saw organisations as complex they both believed that they were understandable by the higher orders and that they could impose their order on their subordinates. In a stable environment over time we could perhaps approximate to a full understanding of the organisation's activity, but that requires one major commodity: time. The rate of change now imposed upon our companies makes the total comprehension of the total task by senior management impossible. Furthermore, as Kanter[2] has pointed out, 'the mean time between decisions is greater than the mean time between surprises':

$$MTBD > MTBS$$

In other words, where we have cumbersome, top-heavy decision-making structures, by the time that a decision has been made the world has changed and the information on which the decision was based has also changed, which thereby invalidates the decision – a powerful argument for decision making being as close to the point of service or production as possible.

Such a discussion may appear rather academic for the busy manager. However, it does raise a fundamental confusion in the minds of many managers of businesses today, fighting for competitive advantage, increased profits and a future. Many of our attempts to regenerate our companies use the same assumptions and solutions as those two significant characters we have paraphrased in the introduction to this chapter. We continue to seek greater efficiency, greater order and the greater fulfilment of our will as though the world was not changing. We concentrate on what we know rather than the uncertain world of the unknown.

To what extent is your organisation characterised by these descriptions?

As we have seen in Chapter 1, innovation is an uncertain process. In many ways it is chaotic, difficult to encourage and difficult to define; it is not susceptible to the ordered structuring which characterises so many of our organisations.

In a company seminar we ran, we asked a team of directors to define the characteristics of an innovator. They came up with:

- free thinker;
- loner;
- nonconformist;
- doesn't take 'no' for an answer;
- high energy;
- can withstand failure;
- can withstand criticism;

- intelligent;
- unstructured;
- constantly questioning.

This company needed innovation, its products were declining, a new technology was wholly changing their business. We asked them how a person with the characteristics they had defined as those of an innovator would survive in their company. 'With great difficulty', they replied. The performance appraisal system would mark him or her down, merit pay would be small, any failure would be dealt with severely, and so on. Without radical organisational change there is unlikely to be much effective innovation in this company.

How well does your organisation tolerate the innovator?

It is a strange paradox that in the West our economic system rests upon free competition, allowing anyone to set up a company to compete with the great and the mighty organisations of the world. In this way new ideas and innovations can come to the fore, old habits can be challenged, and a wide range of consumer choice ensured. This whole process could in the first instance seem inefficient in terms of duplicated effort and resources, yet it is highly effective for the consumer, the economy and the shareholder. However, within our organisations we most often apply a radically different model, one in fact which closely approximates to that of a planned economy.

Internally, companies require order, efficiency and no duplication of effort: the very attributes that are seen as so inefficient in the Eastern European states. Having worked as consultants and teachers in a great many organisations, we have come to the conclusion that so often the efficiency orientation in so many organisations is counterproductive and ineffective; certainly ineffective if we are to regenerate flexible innovative organisations. The paradox, therefore, is between understanding free market economics on a national scale and practising the 'planned economy' inside most of our corporations.

Before we throw out the baby with the bath water, we need to establish the fact that even the most innovative organisations have to produce efficiently the products of those innovations. This may well require the use of ordered processes and systems. In Chapter 6 we develop the major theme that one of the greatest challenges for the organisation which is innovating and managing change is the maintenance of one part of the organisation to continue to produce those cash-generating products alongside the haphazard chaos of the innovation.

The development of organisations

How is it, then, that organisations are created, grow and develop products or services which the market demands, yet then build into themselves the very barriers which prevent them from developing the new ideas, products and processes upon which their survival depends?

One interesting way of looking at the development of organisations is depicted by Valerie Stewart in her book *Change: The Challenge for Management*.[3] She sees three major phases through which organisations must inevitably pass if they are to survive: pioneering, systemisation and integration (Fig. 2.1).

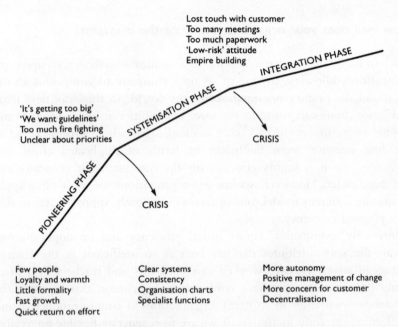

Fig. 2.1 The evolution of organisations

The pioneering phase is the period of high innovation, new products, processes and services which are developed and honed for the marketplace. The group has a clear and distinctive mission, and enthusiasm and dedication are high. Once the product has demonstrated its worth in the marketplace there is often fast growth and a quick return on effort, and everyone mucks in to achieve the common cause. Such groups are usually led by an entrepreneur who is totally dedicated to the organisation, leading from the front and working with little formality, structure or system. The organisational structure, such as it is, is like a spider's web (Fig. 2.2). Innovation and change are vital for survival. There is no prior success that

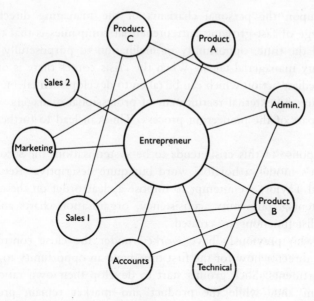

Fig. 2.2 A typical pioneering organisation structure

anyone can cling to; future success is all that can count. The overriding ethos must be that it takes whatever it does to succeed.

Example
A small group of scientists eight years ago left ICI disenchanted with not being able to develop what they considered to be a potential coating product for the construction industry. After four years during which they made a meagre living the product was approved and sales took off. The founder is the managing director, finance director and the hub of the cartwheel which is the shape of his organisation. With rapidly growing success, needing more people, contracting gangs and more research, the organisation is under great strain. The problem is how to loosen that being 'the centre of everything' and still ensure that the now seven years of hard labour will not be wasted by the ineffectiveness of others.

Stewart sees that crisis is pretty well inevitable as with growth and product success the organisation necessarily becomes larger. The newer recruits have little knowledge of or empathy with the pioneers who struggled against all odds to get the product to the market in the right time scale and at an economic cost.

Cries go up that the company is getting too big, guidelines are needed, there is too much fire-fighting, too many people are involved in too many things and other areas are completely ignored. Priorities become unclear as the central figure loses touch with his or her burgeoning organisation. The response to such cries may be to fight against them, but there is a certain inevitability in that the larger an organisation becomes the less it can rely upon the personal charisma of the managing director. One disadvantage of fast-growing entrepreneurial companies is that they have rarely had the time, opportunity or inclination to purposefully grow or develop any managerial talent. When the crisis comes there is often very little immediate action which can be taken to develop such talent, and they may require the external recruitment of professional managers who have not been part of the pioneering process. This can lead to further conflict and crisis.

The response to this crisis tends to be systemisation, the second phase in Stewart's model: a horrible word but quite descriptive. Returning to Weber and Taylor, we attempt to impose a clear order on the company. Clear systems, conformity, consistency, organisation charts and, above all, specialist functions are created.

Those who previously have worked under the close control of the managing director now for the first time have an opportunity to run their own departments. Such groups start to develop their own rationale and momentum and, while the product and market remain pretty well unchanged, business benefit can be gained from this form of subdivision: benefits such as the clarification of the priority functions and the development of the process which delivers the product to the customer. The danger signals start to become major once the rationale and momentum of the functions outweigh those of the organisation as a whole. Managing the boundaries and the integration of the functions becomes less important than managing the survival of the functions themselves. It is then easy to see how the functions are able to move off in their own direction to continue to justify their growth and existence.

Example

In the 1960s and 1970s many large companies built up central data-processing (DP) departments. As mainframe computers became more powerful, this led to the power rise of the DP function. Anyone wanting computer services was told that the DP department were very busy, totally committed and unlikely to address the problem for many months. These people were powerful; the blood of the organisation (information) was pumped around by their heart (the mainframe) according to their architecture (systems design). The development of personal computers has rapidly changed this power base. Now a DP department which wishes to survive is out there with the users, suggesting ideas and applications, as most of what was centrally controlled technology is now available for a few thousand pounds.

This has represented a major shift in attitude and activity for computer specialists. They had started to believe that *they* were the customer; you went to them, pleading for help; you asked, they gave (maybe). Now the tables are turned. The users are the internal customers and if DP don't deliver the users go elsewhere. There has been a radical change in the distribution of organisational power.

Many observers of organisations have noted that those who are good at pioneering are rarely good at sustaining the productive process. Efficient manufacturing requires a detailed and complex order if resource utilisation (machines, raw materials and people) is to be optimised. Therefore systems and procedures are helpful to move us from the state of discovery and development to a well-organised, efficient productive process. The systems we impose have a necessary function in executing our innovation. If we wish to produce millions of model T Fords of set design then many of the features of the classic bureaucracy need to be instilled in the organisation.

The systems are rarely sensitive to the outside world. They are designed on the premise that there is a market for the product and all that has to be done is to manufacture it efficiently.

Example: systemisation in practice

(a) *Production department*

In the production of light bulbs it is efficient to have long production runs. Therefore when Sainsburys order half a million 60W bulbs and half a million 100W bulbs the production planning department decides that Sainsburys can have the 60W bulbs this month and the 100W bulbs next month. The problem is that Sainsburys wish to sell both types side by side and do not wish to stock millions of bulbs while other types are being produced.

(b) *Personnel department*

A major software house, part of a larger conglomerate, is losing software engineers and is finding recruitment difficult. The job specification is changing rapidly and there is a heavy workload. The MD suspects that the compensation and benefit package is not competitive. He asks the corporate personnel department to undertake a market survey. The personnel department's reply was to ask the MD to submit a revised job description to the central job evaluation committee for consideration. Six months later he was still being told that the matter was being progressed.

Both phases described have their parallels in the technology life cycle (see Chapter 1). The initial phase of product innovation is typically the pioneering phase where enthusiasm dominates, often through R&D leadership. Systemisation becomes evident once mass production starts and marketing dominates the firm. As in the previous phase, in time a crisis ensues. The company loses touch with the customer, conformity to the system is more important than meeting a customer need, and energy is expended in fighting internal battles. The orientation of the organisation has become internally focused. It is this crisis which is the crux of the problem facing many companies which are currently attempting to manage the introduction of new technology. In the technology life cycle complacency sets in; the orientation has become that of production and finance. The company introduces ever more rigid and detailed forms of cost reduction which are necessary to remain competitive with a mature technology in an often saturated market. But if the company is to avoid the inevitable despair and decline, it has to refind and recreate that early pioneering entrepreneurial spirit which was lost as it became more and more fossilised by its own systems.

The third phase Stewart calls integration, which represents the greatest challenge of all. It is the crisis which demands integration which is the central purpose of this book. The systems have not delivered organisations with sufficient flexibility or future orientation to survive in the long term. We need to integrate the necessary systems with the bringing forward of the future; systems and the features of the pioneering phase living uneasily together. It is not merely the restarting of the cycle. It is rather the integration of advanced manufacturing or service systems and procedures with the relentless pursuit of incremental improvement of current methods and the search for, and development of, new products and processes ever more quickly and flexibly.

Stewart sees this integrated organisation as comprising more autonomous groups, each having a much closer concern for their customers but well able to positively manage complex change requirements.

Any model of organisations is bound in part to simplify the total reality of a company. One of the impressions often given is that if only we can get to this new desired state then we shall have arrived and all we have to do is to manage that state in a maintenance mode. The managers of a nearly dead shipbuilding company lamented to us that the changeover to building highly complex oil-exploration vessels was just to tide them over until the orders for big bulk carriers came back; they never did.

Managing technological change requires the continuing management of tension and disparate interests. The tension is between investment in the current and the promise of the future. It is a creative tension which is productive but at times difficult to steer and manage. An innovative organisation is of itself of limited value if it cannot also maximise the advantage from that innovation. As we have seen, that requires a different style and approach from the organisation which is structured solely to manage the present. Many a commentator has noted that Clive Sinclair is a genius of innovation but has failed consistently to deliver the product the customer wants.

Summary

Organisations change and often we do not understand the reasons why. There is no ideal steady organisational state; it must reflect the needs of the business and be responsive to change. There is a certain inevitability to how organisations change, particularly as they grow in size and become more mature. The questions for managers are:

- How does your organisation treat and support innovators?
- Are managers conscious of the need to balance efficiency with effectiveness?
- Do your systems support or retard change?
- Do your managers confuse conformity with effectiveness?

The entrepreneur within the large organisation

We see the entrepreneur as a person who has an unshakable vision of what he or she wishes to accomplish and the total dedication and energy to achieve it. For too long we have supposed that such behaviour is not possible within the larger company, so that the activity of developing new products and processes has become a systematised affair with research, development, planning and engineering functions each having a clear and separate role. This is often seen as a sequence in which R&D develop the technology, which then gets handed over to engineering, from there to production and finally to the sales department, which sells it in an unsuspecting marketplace. On further examination, however, it is clear that there are many large organisations which have had, and continue to have, an impressive record for both the development and the implementation of new products and processes. It is from an examination of these companies, such as Hewlett-Packard, 3M and Matsushita, that we can find out how entrepreneurs or intrapreneurs can be highly successful within the right corporate culture.

Intrapreneurship

'Intrapreneurs' is a word coined to describe those individuals who are or can be entrepreneurs within the large corporation. The term came from Gifford Pinchot's book, *Intrapreneuring*.[5] It is written from the point of view of the individual who has some sparkle and looks beyond the constraints of the organisation to develop internal space and freedom to create, innovate and drive through new ideas and products.

Much attention has been given to this concept, particularly in the USA, where so many examples of highly expensive unsuccessful projects have been catalogued. Various attempts have been made to package the intrapreneurship concept into a series of proprietary approaches marketed by trainers and consultants. The pitfall for such approaches is that they have attempted to systematise an organic and uncertain process. We cannot make individuals innovate; all we can do is ensure that we remove the barriers and provide a supportive environment.

The breadth of skills of the intrapreneur is wide. This is the gap that has to be spanned if we are to manage technological change successfully (Fig. 2.3). He suggests that we may have no shortage of ideas people and planners, or any lack of operational management expertise for managing processes. The challenge is managing the integration of this wide diversity of expertise. It lies between those who can visualise the future product and those who have the practical skills to enable it to become a marketable product.

There is increasing awareness that the attributes of the people who can achieve this and the organisational climate in which it can happen are a far cry from that model of organisational stability so firmly implanted in many of our managerial brains. Tom Peters, in his book *Thriving on Chaos*, uses the word 'revolution' in his subtitle to convey the radical nature of the managerial change demanded by innovation.

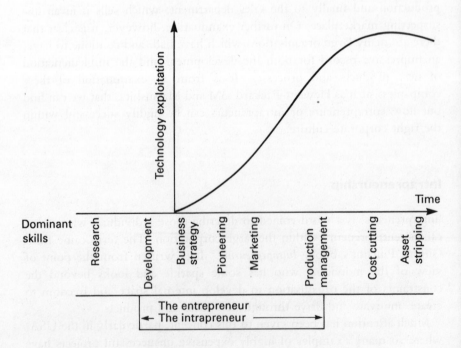

Fig. 2.3 The breadth of skills of the entrepreneur/intrapreneur

Pinchot has ten commandments for the intrapreneur:
(1) Come to work each day willing to be fired.
(2) Circumvent any orders aimed at stopping your dream.
(3) Do any job needed to make your project work, regardless of your job description.
(4) Find people to help you.
(5) Follow your intuition about the people you choose.
(6) Work underground as long as you can; publicity triggers the corporate immune mechanism.
(7) Never bet on a race unless you are running in it.
(8) Remember it is easier to ask for forgiveness than for permission.
(9) Be true to your goals, but be realistic about the ways to achieve them.
(10) Honour your sponsors.

Alongside these we can place the ten commandments for the survivalists in our organisations:
(1) Come to work each day with the prime objective of not being fired.
(2) Obey all orders even if you don't agree with them.
(3) Work to your job description and do not be seen to step out of line.
(4) Be careful whom you work for. Make sure their stars are rising lest any muck sticks on you.
(5) Work with and for those with power and influence. Ignore all good ideas championed by the unfavoured.
(6) Brag about the first signs of any success. This will demonstrate that you are keen and committed. It stops anyone else claiming that the success is theirs, and it will also allow you the opportunity to blame others if and when it goes wrong.
(7) Back safety and security; above all don't gamble; failure is unforgivable.
(8) You won't need to ask for permission, as all your duties and limits of authority will be in your job description.
(9) As survival is your main goal, always be true to whomever appears to have most power and influence. Don't rock the boat and always take the line of least resistance.
(10) Honour your sponsors, i.e. those on whose favour your job rests.

There is one difference between the two sets of rules: organisational values. What is it that this organisation rewards, sponsors and encourages? Pinchot's whole book is based on the view that organisations do not value those attributes of a change and innovation orientation. He therefore instructs his students in a process which approximates to guerilla warfare, if we use the parallel of political as opposed to organisational change.

For the organisation wishing to become more innovative many of the

Table 2.1 The qualities which differentiate managers, entrepreneurs and intrapreneurs

	Manager	Entrepreneur	Intrapreneur
Individual Drive	To be successful within the existing system and structure	To realise his/her dream	To maximise the corporate resources to realise his/her dream
Management Style	Formal, delegating, fixed performance measures	Hands on – does what it takes to keep the business running	Hands on, team leader, highly protective of the team against the mainstream organisation
Management Skills	Formally trained	Unlikely to have formal skills	Highly developed project management skills
Focus	Inward/short term	Outward/long term	Can mix both inward and outward/long term
Conformity	High	Low	Low
Risk orientation	Low	High	High
Customer orientation	Formal through marketing dept	Working directly with customers	Direct to customers using marketing if willing

Status orientation	Status conscious	Disinterested	Opts out of formal status structure
Decision-making	Decisive and convergent	Uncompromising and divergent	Adaptive and divergent
Thinking-style	Rational/political	Intuitive	Intuitive/political
Tolerance of ambiguity	Low	High	Very high
Typical Team Types	Chairman/company worker	Shapes/Resource investigator/Ideas person	Shape/Resource investigator/ideas person.
Commitment	To incremental improvement	Own goals	Company mission and values
Rewards	Expects to be highly rewarded if achieves measures of performance	Expects to be well rewarded if successful	Would like to be well rewarded if successful but is doubtful whether achievement will be recognised.

ideas of intrapreneurship are attractive. This has led some organisations and indeed consultants to suppose that one can set up a *structure* to identify and grow intrapreneurs. Here we have something of a contradiction. Can one set up a structure or system to defy structures and systems? The answer is in all probability 'no'. Rather we can use our understanding and insight into the characteristics of intrapreneurs, entrepreneurs and managers to inform our decisions on recruitment and how we structure our organisation (Table 2.1).

If we examine the most recent past of many of our companies it is hardly surprising that so many of today's managers find concepts of embracing change difficult. With radical manpower reductions having been the norm in so many companies, and the main emphasis having been on almost endless cost reduction, now to command innovation is a tall order. Part of the answer lies in the way we see managerial achievement. Excellence in performing today's tasks is no longer sufficient to ensure executive survival; in addition the extent to which they have contributed to the development of tomorrow has to take increasing weight in our assessment of our managers.

We have to convince our best people that there are positive advantages in sticking with the large company to innovate rather than using the secure climate of the corporation to develop ideas for subsequent execution in a small venture company. In the UK, as well as in the rest of Western Europe, the social and economic climate has moved markedly towards supporting those innovative individuals who wish to set up their own venture companies. Political received wisdom sees the creation of new jobs primarily in the small-business sector. The inducements, therefore, for our best people to leave us are increasing just at the very time when we are recognising their worth to our companies. It is therefore not merely tolerance of the entrepreneur we are proposing; it is rather the wholesale encouragement of such people even if this means that the organisation may become less efficient in some other respect.

If we take Pinchot at his word can we be sure of anything except total anarchy? The key is in the working of creative tension in the organisation. We have seen that we are most unlikely to be able to order, structure or even control innovation. We therefore have a managerial responsibility to:

- be clear about the superordinate goals of the company;
- create and nurture a climate or culture in which the creative can create;
- control the controllable and trust that if 80 per cent of the resources spent on the uncontrollable are effective we are getting a good deal;
- separate out and differentiate between the maintainers and the developers.

The organisation's culture

The organisation whose car park has the spaces closest to the front door reserved for the directors, the next closest for the senior managers, the next for the staff and finally places the visitors (and, who knows, maybe prospective customers) furthest away so that they have to walk through the lot is making a symbolic statement of what it considers important. The manager who says at his appraisal that he has done well, as he has met his budget, and the fact that the division has made such a loss has nothing to do with him is equally expressing what he considers to be important. The receptionist who says, when you ask for the firm's managing partner, that no one has ever told her who he or she is, is expressing the priority that the firm has placed on induction training. These are all expressions of corporate culture.

Organisation culture may be defined as 'the body of norms, assumptions of value and attitudes which affect the actions of employees at all levels and thereby influence the characteristics and behaviour of the organisation'. Ideas about culture have been around for some time, but it is only relatively recently that they have been considered as important and that it has been accepted that we can and should influence and manage the culture of organisations. Much of the inspiration for this has stemmed from the examination of Japanese and leading North American organisations. 'Culture' is so often the word which we use to describe the difference between a UK company and its Japanese counterpart. Culture is not easy to interpret, but it incorporates some useful insights: insights about the relative importance placed upon achieving the organisation's goals as opposed to merely sectional goals; whether dispatching faulty goods is treated as more of a problem than not reaching production targets, and so on.

Against a management tradition of fashion and fad, where techniques have rolled off consultants' tongues with a monotonous regularity, to be picked up by eager managers wanting final solutions to complex and dynamic problems, culture describes a whole range of facets of an organisation, none of which is likely to be changed overnight. It is the combination of this range of facets which makes up an organisation's culture, and only by looking at all its elements are we likely to modify and change our company culture.

What is increasingly certain is that the transformation required for many companies requires major changes to the way they behave. Take, for example, organisations which have moved from the public to the private sector in Japan, France and the UK. New sets of competitive pressures are thrust upon them. The relative emphases that the group places upon customer service, higher standards, profitability, risk and innovation will have to change. Courtaulds annual report states:

Over the next two years we shall be using both the name and the symbol across the group, not only to communicate the fact of change in itself but also to underpin and give expression to the changing 'culture' of the business. Let me explain why I think this changing culture has important and beneficial implications for the Company's future.

C. A. Hogg, Courtaulds Annual Report 1986

The culture of the organisation can be difficult to identify. Organisational structure, history, product and market all have an influence, but above all the management, and in particular the top management, has a major influence upon the culture. Foreign competition in the UK has heightened our awareness of fundamental cultural difference. For example, what is it that distinguishes:

- Nissan from Rover?
- IBM from ICL?
- Yamazaki from GKN?
- Toshiba from Ferguson?

Our research and practical experience confirm that the introduction of technological change often requires fundamental cultural change. Our failure to reap the maximum rewards from our investments is rarely technically rooted; it is managerially and organisationally caused. We have to change the way in which we manage, train, reward and motivate our staff. This should not be seen as an act of managerial altruism alongside a major capital investment; it is rather an organisational imperative, without which we shall be less competitive, less productive and ultimately doomed to failure.

We can look at culture as a set of orientations which can be assessed against each other, against those of our competitors and against where we believe our organisation must be if we are to realise our business strategy. Comparing our products or services with those of our competitors does not give us sufficient information as to where competitive advantage is generated. We must also compare our management practices, our success in innovation, and our success in introducing new technology, a process which Rank Xerox calls competitive benchmarking. In this way we can start to identify where we can gain competitive advantage.

Examples of culture orientations include:

- customer orientation;
- results and performance orientation;
- future orientation;
- cost orientation.

(A full list, with definitions, is presented in Chapter 8.)

It would be nice to think that our organisation could excel at each of the orientations. This is highly unlikely, unless we have unlimited resources and the absence of a keen profitability target. But, like every aspect of management, culture change is about making choices given that our resources are limited. Where can the smallest effort yield the greatest impact on the success of the company? Hence, if we wish the dominant value of the company to be cost saving, then let us not expect the customer to get much attention from the manager who is measured by his success at reducing costs!

Summary

Managing technological change requires resources and priority to be given to managing the culture, as well as the technology itself. The questions for managers are:

- Can we identify our predominant culture alongside those of our competitors?
- Do we currently make attempts to manage the culture alongside the technology?
- How culture-conscious are our managers?

Leadership in innovative organisations

Leadership is fundamental to the culture of an organisation. Of greater importance than any policy or procedure in a company are the behaviour and actions of its leaders. We may say we want innovation and change, but unless we clearly demonstrate by our actions that we are leading that change by our own example, then it is unlikely that much will change. So what sort of leaders are we? There are many ways of categorising leaders; all are approximations. What do we approximate to?

For the purposes of this discussion we shall refer to a simple set of descriptions which are the executive styles portrayed by Edward de Bono in his book *Opportunities*.[6]

The train driver

Trains have schedules. Trains have tracks. The train driver sees his role as taking the train smoothly along the track to meet the schedules. Efficient performance within the established framework is the measure of performance and success. The train driver does not question the schedules or the tracks. He knows he cannot leave the tracks and therefore does not develop any inclination to do so. He deals with problems as they arise in order to restore the schedules.

The doctor

The doctor is a problem solver. He deals in ill health. Unlike the train driver, the doctor does not operate the bodies with which he deals. The doctor realises that bodies are independent and follow their own nature. So the doctor executive is content for each semi-autonomous part of the organisation to go its own way, provided it keeps healthy. This type of leader keeps a close eye on the information which is sent back to him, and as soon as he detects ill health he moves in with his diagnostic kit and recommends treatment. Much depends on what you call success. If the company is smooth running and lacks problems he's a winner. Such a company may well stagnate while its competitors are developing new products and processes. The problem solver is not by nature inclined to seek out opportunities, although he may use much creative thinking in his problem solving.

The farmer

The farmer is the manager who wishes to stay in his own patch. Within the patch he is open to innovation, change and new opportunities. The farmer is an operator, a problem solver and an opportunist. The farmer will seek out opportunities, but only in a defined direction.

The fisherman

The fisherman is the risk taker. He owns no farm. He cannot guarantee that when he ventures out he will return with a catch. He puts down his nets and hopes for the best. He is a pure opportunist. Yet the fisherman is not the gambler which he may at first appear. He has invested his skill, experience and equipment. Through such investment he reduces uncertainty and increases the chance of substantial payoff.

De Bono summarises his four characters as follows:

- Train driver: Let me carry out to perfection the assigned tasks in the established system.
- Doctor: Let me keep the system healthy and functioning well by detecting and solving any problems as they arise.

- Farmer: Let me get the maximum yield that I can out of this established area of operation.
- Fisherman: Let me put myself in such a position that I can look for and follow up any opportunity as it arises.

It is unlikely that an organisation will find the means for its own survival if it does not have in its senior management team a good proportion of farmers and fishermen: farmers to champion the inexorable incremental improvement of every activity and task in the current portfolio of products and processes; and fishermen to seek out new opportunities which will ensure the future of the company. There will be a tension between the two. Who should have the resources? How do we make decisions on the competing claims?

Leadership in the innovative company has to become a sharing between the demands of the future and the demands of the present. There is no right balance between the two; that can be decided only in the light of the particular company's situation and priorities. What we can be sure of, however, is that the two will be in tension. This tension has to be managed if opportunities are going to be maximised.

The rate at which new models and variants of products are launched on the marketplace is increasing. The Japanese consumer electronics industry is becoming a short-cycle fashion industry, with some products being revised twice annually. The Japanese use the concept of TAT, otherwise known as turn-around time. TAT is defined as the time between the perception of the need or demand for a new product and its mass availability in the shops. Matsushita currently hold the record, with a TAT of under five months. This gives little or no time for the following competitor to catch up.

The opportunities to separate our two key activities of farming and fishing are becoming reduced. The two activities have to become more integrated, if not merged.

Summary

The demand is for dual-perspective management, one eye looking at the present, the other on the future. The dimensions of the two are very different. It is so easy to promise a new product in two years' time; we are often hopelessly optimistic about what will be achieved a long way from the here and now. Innovative leadership has to keep both views firmly in perspective.

Questions for managers are:

- How many fishermen and farmers do you have among your managers?

- How many train drivers do you have?
- How do short-term perspectives clash with long-term ones in your organisation?

The business focus of the innovative organisation

If we believe that the innovative organisation is one bubbling with ideas, anarchists undermining authority positions and skunkworks (unsanctioned activity) playing an ever-increasing role, then we must pay particular attention to how such a group can possibly have any coherence, direction or overriding sense of purpose. The answer lies in the diagram of the two ships which Tom Peters[7] draws for his audiences. The bottom of the hull represents the foundation of the organisation, its major purpose and its direction of movement. The rest of the vessel is there to achieve that overriding purpose. He sees that in many organisations the water line is very high. In other words, nearly everything that the organisation does is deemed to be sacrosanct, beyond question and challenge. The successful organisations are those which have a low water line. In other words, everything that the organisation does to support its principal purpose and direction should be open to question and challenge. The analogy leaves us with the question of how we should determine and describe what is the hull, that part of the vessel which is not up for grabs, questioning or undermining.

It is not the intention to give a long treatise on the function and purpose of strategic management. However, if an organisation is to have coherence and purpose in the chaotic environment which we have described, then it is our contention that considerable top management effort has to be put into determining that overall direction and purpose. Such a strategy is not an empty rhetorical gesture; rather it is the touchstone which is universally accepted throughout the organisation and by which we can judge whether our efforts are in line with the company or not. It is precisely because of the increased uncertainty, the increased flexibility and the very nature of innovation that we need a positive means of delimiting our endeavours from those of others and ensuring that throughout all the diversity there is a strong thread of coherence. It is what Peters and Waterman[8] have called the loose–tight relationship. It is the firm setting of the boundaries or the hull, using the nautical analogy, but within that framework the maximising of our endeavours to achieve our goals.

Top-down or bottom-up innovation?

Ideas about business strategy often give the impression of technological innovation being principally a top-down affair. If the top management has a future perspective then the fishermen among them will seek out new opportunities for the organisation to embrace. This is in part true, but no management team has a monopoly on ideas and wisdom. Increasingly one might argue that managers are going to be less well equipped than young technologists with state-of-the-art understanding of their subject. As we have already seen, the pace of change is such that it is impossible for top management to understand, let alone initiate, the change required.

We must, therefore, see the innovative organisation as one which allows a free flow of ideas from the top down and the bottom up. Such organisations have processes of dealing with both to ensure that the position of the person who champions an idea does not make the idea more or less worthy of consideration.

The implication for management of embracing this two-way exchange of ideas is that another dual focus is required. A major investment decision in a new product developed by R&D may well have its origins in a junior group of technologists. Once the decision to invest in this idea is taken, top management commitment is required to effect successful implementation. The 'bottom-up' focus requires managers to act as helpers and facilitators to encourage and stimulate ideas for improvement. The 'top-down' focus requires managers to effect the change through clarity of direction, provision of the necessary resources and monitoring and controlling progress.

The nature of decision making

There is a growing body of opinion which suggests that decision making based purely on rational and logical criteria is inadequate. Peters and Waterman[9] claim that '. . . detached, analytical justifications for all decisions . . . has arguably led us seriously astray'. The problem is that purely analytical approaches to decision making increase our skill in ordering the alternatives but diminish our understanding of the nature of the problem, how we identify problems and how we implement our decisions.

One way of looking at our decision-making style is shown in Fig. 2.4. The first of the two dimensions describes the extent to which people look at situations as a whole or seek to break them down into their constituent elements. The second axis describes the extent to which we look at situ-

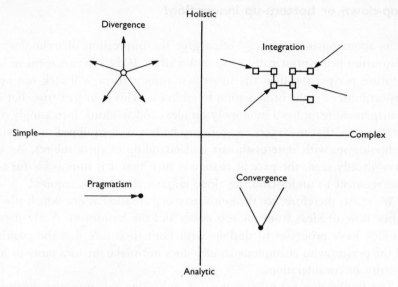

Fig. 2.4 Decision-making styles

ations in a complex, interconected way or simply as they appear on the surface. Using this matrix we can pick out different approaches to decision making.

The four styles are each a function of how much data is used and the approach taken. The analytical approach is represented by two styles: pragmatism and convergence. Both rely on a logical analysis, though the pragmatist takes the shorter route, using far less data. Divergence and integration represent more intuitive styles, depending often on an unstructured approach. Whilst the divergent decision maker moves out from the central theme to seek ideas, the integrator starts with a wide array of ideas and forms patterns and networks with them. Both these styles give decisions which often embrace new conceptual possibilities, and which are open to change when the situation changes.

The innovative organisation needs to recognise intuitive as well as rational/logical decision-making processes. The example below is a vivid example of where 'rational' decision making overruled 'intuitive' decision making, to the severe disadvantage of a major bank.

Example
A major British bank which has always been at the forefront in adopting advanced information technology was one of the first to build up a network of the earliest forms of automated teller machines, or ATMs. These were basically cash-dispensing machines and, once installed, they failed to achieve the utilisation or customer acceptability expected. As more sophisticated machines became available the bank decided that they would not

invest further, and adopted a 'wait and see' policy to any further capital expenditure. The decision was soon challenged by the rapid take-up of ATMs, particularly by the bank's closest rival, which installed well over 100 machines over a two-year period, thereby seriously threatening the bank's competitive position.

The question is how the bank, from a position of technological superiority, could lose it so quickly through one decision. To answer the question we have to look at the 'rational' decision-making process, which clearly showed that the initial investment in cash machines was poor and the 'wait and see' policy correct. Information technology investment decisions were justified on the basis of back-office cost savings such as reduced manpower and greater transaction-processing efficiency. These internally focused decision criteria are quite rational. What they lack is customer focus. A new service to the customer is unlikely to be justified by rational but inwardly looking criteria.

Failure as part of the road to success

Change and innovation are inherently risky: risky for the company, but particularly risky for the individual. Most companies can withstand some degree of failure, but many individuals cannot, as it will blight their career chances, destroy their merit increases, and limit their scope to take risks again. Step out of line and the big shovel comes down; it hurts! Unless we have recruited a mass of masochists, then basic animal behaviour will suggest that we are unlikely to try willingly again! In so many companies in which we work this attitude is dominant, and the values, systems and procedures of the organisation only reinforce it. The problem for many is that management is seen as a process of ensuring compliance with preset tasks and actions; too few of us can cope with the uncertainty of risk. The term 'management' itself has become associated with control and constraint rather than the direction and empowering of others, which are more associated with the term 'leadership'.

'Risk' we have defined as the willingness to accept losses on activities which have a low probability of a high return on investment. We must therefore accept those losses if we are to gain the rewards. Some failure must be a necessary consequence of our endeavours.

If we run a suggestion scheme, then, do we have a view on what the score rate should be for major ideas? Should it be 5 per cent, or even 10 per cent? Either way we need some good strategies to ensure that the originators of the other 90 or 95 per cent are not demotivated and made to feel worthless, so that the flow of ideas dribbles to a halt. Is it not through some failure that success comes? Peters suggests that managers should support past failures rather than brush them under the carpet and pretend they did not happen. The need to positively manage failure increases as complexity and the need to be highly responsive increase.

These lead to a necessary increase in the incidence of failure and the need to recognise it, learn from it, but also accept that in an uncertain world it is inevitable.

Innovation through acquisition

An attractive alternative to changing existing organisations is to acquire new ones and bulldoze the old ones. If the right ones are chosen, those which have pioneered their product, then all the pain and resistance we might otherwise encounter in our own well-established business seem to be overcome. However, we have to be most careful that we do not replace one type of pain for another, that is, the pain which comes from deciding (if we decide at all) how we are to manage our new acquisition. All the evidence suggests that, given half a chance, every functional head in the acquiring company will want to impose their will upon the fledgling company: financial controls, decision-making levels, interference, all in the name of maximising our investment. Or is it rather maximising our own territory, establishing our hegemony over the domain lest they rise to challenge the existing order?

Example

An engineering company was recently taken over by a large manufacturing conglomerate. The small company produces a range of high-quality precision components for the aerospace industry. During the first two years of being part of the larger group, the company grew and prospered, largely left to get on on its own. The second year's financial results were so good that they appeared as a separate item on the group's accounts. The chairman asked his board colleagues for more information about this rising star. He got little, so decided to go and have a look for himself. He was on the whole pleased with what he saw, but a little concerned at the apparent disorder of the place. Soon the other members of the board were also requesting visits so that they could answer the chairman's questions. The finance director was appalled by the cost and finance structure and immediately put in a team to enforce the group standard. The personnel department insisted on the group grading structure, and the data-processing department on integrated systems. And so it went on: forced systemisation from the centre. The MD became quite despondent; every decision was challenged by someone upholding the group standard. Ironically the company's performance dipped in the third year below the threshold which registers it separately in the group accounts. It is the MD's view that much of the reason for the decline in performance was due to the prime customer becoming group headquarters rather than the users of their quality products.

Features of the innovative organisation

The patterns which emerge from successful companies can be categorised by a set of common features. Alongside these we can equally well list those barriers to effective technological change.

Support features

Company vision

Innovative top management teams have a clear vision and direction for their company. That vision incorporates a premium on the future development of the company and the management act to reinforce that vision.

Customer orientation

Innovation is closely tied to the marketplace. It is not compartmentalised such that, once the product is developed, the marketing function is then given the task of marketing it.

Technology orientation

The company, and particularly its top team, see technology as a powerful resource in gaining competitive advantage. Technology learning and experimentation are encouraged and management's vision of the company embraces a view of the future place of technology in the company and how this is to be achieved.

Organisation structures

The total organisation will be flat, probably having no more than five layers from top to bottom. Much of the activity of the company will be run by small multidisciplinary project teams. Operating companies will be kept as small as possible and will be given a high degree of local autonomy in the running of their affairs.

Internal competition

Encouragement will be given to internal competition between project teams to reduce the risk of failure, but also to encourage a constructive competitive spirit. A diversity of approaches is necessary if the company is going to have sufficient flexibility to meet the market challenge.

Acceptance of the unorthodox

The organisation will have a high level of tolerance to the unorthodox. Plainly this cannot be a licence to do anything one wishes, and therefore it has to be supported by a clear vision and direction. Part of this may well include the ability for certain groups to undertake, for part of their time, unsanctioned activity with a budget allocation to match. This is popularly called skunkworks.

Positive management of change implementation

The company will place particular emphasis on *how* new products and processes are implemented. Again the role of the small, flexible team is crucial.

Positive rewards

To reinforce the behaviour we wish to encourage we need to tailor our system of rewards to successful innovation.

Barriers

The most common characteristics of companies which are poor at innovation can be described as follows.

The lack of a future orientation

Top management has become isolated both from the firm and from the marketplace. There is no future vision and executive concerns are primarily operational.

Intolerance of 'fanatics'

Entrepreneurs do not seem to fit in with the organisation and hence they do not stay or just acquiesce. Fitting in with the dominant team is far more important than stepping out of line and developing a new product.

Accounting practices

Accounting practices which concentrate solely upon measuring cost saving and efficiency improvement will strongly influence individuals to pursue these goals. 'You can innovate as long as it does not cost money or the payback is over six months' is a hollow plea for change and renewal.

Excessive rationalism

If there is no space for intuitive, explorative and developmental behaviour then innovation will be retarded. Innovation is not an entirely rational process; it requires acceptance of risk, uncertainty, flair and conviction.

Inappropriate incentives

As with accounting practices and excessive rationalism, incentives to groups or individuals which reinforce short-term actions give a counter-message to innovation. If the operators are paid large additional sums for increasing output this will speak much more loudly than exhortations to reduce the reject rate, increase machine utilisation and improve quality.

Summary

Organisations are particularly difficult to classify, given their enormous diversity. As we learn more about the process of innovation we start to identify those characteristics which are barriers to the innovative company. Removal of these barriers does not guarantee success; rather it increases a group's chances of being able to constantly improve and renew itself.

We do need to spend time looking at our existing organisation to see to what extent we positively encourage innovation or, on the other hand, positively discourage innovation. We can do this by examining the concepts explored in this chapter.

Senior management cannot be neutral with respect to the organisation's environment. It is positive action which is required, and there can be no fence-sitting. The board is waiting to see whether this new product will be successful or not; by sitting on the fence it is acting as a negative force.

References

1. Weber, M. (1970) *Essays in Sociology*, ed. Gerth & Mills. RKP.
2. Kanter, R. M. (1984) *The Change Masters: Corporate Entrepreneurs at Work*. George Allen and Unwin.
3. Stewart, V. (1983) *Change: The Challenge for Management*. McGraw-Hill.

4. Handy, C. (1976) *Understanding Organisations*. Pelican.
5. Pinchot, G. (1985) *Intrapreneuring*. Harper and Row.
6. De Bono, E. (1978) *Opportunities*. Pelican.
7. Peters, T. (1988) *Thriving on Chaos*. Macmillan.
8. Peters, T. J. and Waterman, R. H. (1982) *In Search of Excellence*. Harper and Row.

3 Technical change and the business

The first two chapters have exposed the dilemma of managing technical change. Chapter 1 emphasised the need to analyse the changing technological environment in which a business operates and its impact on the scope for growth within an industry. The strategic implications of technical progress were stressed. This is primarily an intellectual exercise and one which perforce *must* be a major concern of top management. Only they can determine the main framework for what the organisation should do. They must establish the demarcations within which the majority of operational decisions must be taken. It implies strong *top-down* management. Taken to its extreme it might describe a highly *dirigiste* style of management.

Chapter 2, on the other hand, examined the nature of effective change within an organisation. It stressed the importance of a culture within which individuals or internal entrepreneurs can initiate innovations and bring them to a successful conclusion. It was noted that the complexity and rapidity of change are such that top management cannot comprehend the totality of the situations facing them. They must rely on *bottom-up* management and assume the role of facilitators. Taken to its extreme this might be thought to describe a state approaching anarchy.

The challenge of managing technical change is the achievement of a symbiosis between these two approaches.

In our studies of companies we find that they can be categorised broadly as follows:

(a) *Non-innovative*. In these, technical change has largely been ignored except on an occasional ad hoc basis in response to competitive pressure. In general they have continued with their traditional activities largely unchanged, often resulting in a severe erosion of their profits.

(b) *Strategy centred*. These firms have concentrated upon strategic analysis and detailed corporate planning. This approach, prevalent amongst large companies in the 1970s, often failed to achieve the desired results because of an inability to translate plans into effective action. In recent years many of these companies have abandoned formal corporate planning and reduced the size of their head offices. In their place they have instituted a system of strategic management, with more decisions delegated to the managements of strategic business units (SBUs). Although this decentralisation has effected some improvement in moving decision making closer to the market, it is only a partial solution, since the managements of the SBUs have often failed to introduce into them the conditions necessary for innovation.

(c) *Entrepreneurial*. These companies, usually small initially, have focused on the exploitation of technology. Many of them have failed due to their inability to control costs or to market their products effectively. In many cases they have been obsessed by the technology upon which their initial success was based and ignored the competitive potential of a new technology. Thus, for example, both Hughes and Sylvania, which in 1955 were respectively first and fourth in world transistor manufacture based on germanium, failed to appreciate the potential of silicon and within five years ceased to be amongst the leaders in the industry.

(d) *Innovative*. These are the relatively few companies which have been able to maintain a sustained high growth rate by responding to technical change, but within a coherent corporate strategy.

The characteristics of this last category, the innovative firm, are shown in Fig. 3.1, where they are contrasted with those of the more traditional company. It will be observed that the management focus in the innovative firm is on people, whereas the traditional company emphasises systems.

The problem is further complicated by the need to maintain an ongoing activity at the same time as the introduction of technical change. Thus a radical new product incorporating a new technology must be developed alongside incremental improvements to an existing product. A new operational system has to be introduced, for example a production system, without causing undue disruption to the processes in which it is being incorporated. This often means that the innovative firm should adopt different managerial styles in different parts of its business. This adds a further complexity to the management of change. Our emphasis is upon the management of the technical change, since this is the aspect where companies so often fail due to the vested interests of the existing activities in which most of the past investment has been concentrated. But the concerns of the existing business cannot be neglected. The process is analogous with a heart transplant. Without it the patient will die, but perhaps not for some time. If the operation is not carried out skilfully the patient will die on the operating table, and there is always the risk of rejection if the systems are not matched. So it is with technical change.

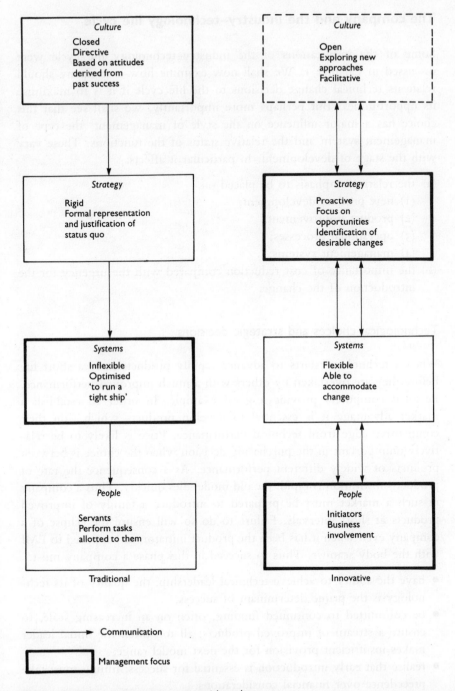

Fig. 3.1 Traditional and innovative managerial emphases

The company and the industry–technology life cycle

Some of the implications of the industry–technology life cycle were discussed in Chapter 1. We shall now examine how a company should relate its technical change decisions to the life cycle if it is to maximise its opportunities. But perhaps more importantly, we shall see that this choice has a major influence on the style of management, the type of management system and the relative status of the functions. These vary with the stage of development. In particular it affects:

(a) the relative emphasis to be placed on –
    (1) new product development;
    (2) product improvement;
    (3) operational processes;
    (4) management systems;
(b) the importance of cost reduction compared with the urgency for the introduction of the change.

Technological choices and strategic decisions

When a technology starts to advance rapidly products have a short life before they are overtaken by others with a much improved performance. Personal computers provide a good example. In order to establish a market advantage it is essential to develop products which gain their competitive edge from technical performance. Price is likely to be relatively unimportant in the purchasing decision when the choice is between products of widely different performance. As a consequence the rate of product substitution is rapid: the old model dies quickly. Thus a company in such a market must be prepared to introduce a family of improved products at short intervals. Failure to do so will ensure the eclipse of a company even when it has been the product initiator, as happened to EMI with the body scanner. Thus to succeed in this phase a company must:

- have the ability to achieve technical leadership; the quality of its technology is the prime determinant of success;
- be committed to continued funding, often on an increasing scale, to ensure a stream of improved products; all too often the initial leader makes insufficient provision for the next model range;
- realise that early introduction is essential for success; timing must take precedence over financial considerations.

The importance of this last point is vital. At a time of rapid progress major technical uncertainties are unavoidable. Their resolution is likely to add to the development costs, which are frequently considerably higher than anticipated. Corners have to be cut in order to solve problems quickly; this is expensive. In many companies the natural instinct is to attempt to control the costs, particularly when they are escalating. Almost inevitably this delays the product launch. However, the reduction in profit from delay, thereby reducing the already short product life, will usually be much greater than that resulting from a development cost overrun. One example of a typical electronic product with a five-year life showed the following relationship: a 50 per cent increase in development cost resulted in a 3.5 per cent profit loss; a 9 per cent increase in product cost resulted in a 22 per cent profit loss; and six months' delay in launch resulted in a 33 per cent profit loss. This example can only be an illustration, and the relative effect is sensitive to the characteristics of the product. Nevertheless, it does make the point that in this early stage of the life cycle *time* is likely to be much more important than *cost*. Management must assess: how sensitive the profitability of an envisaged development is to:

(a) development cost escalation;

(b) product cost;

(c) launch delay.

The minimisation of development time does not depend solely upon the availability of finance. The quality of the development team, both technically and managerially, is critical. Decisions must be technically sound and made quickly. These traits are typical of an informal, entrepreneurial style of management where decision making is delegated to a project manager within a supportive organisation. It is to be expected that a high status would be accorded to the R&D director within the informal company hierarchy.

As the technology continues to move up the life cycle the focus of technology must change. With lengthening product lives, market segmentation and the increased emphasis on product improvement the contribution from the marketing department increases in importance. There is less need for urgency and profit becomes more sensitive to cost considerations. It is during this phase that more formal systems are introduced, often with resistance from R&D. Attention may have to be paid to the relationship between R&D and marketing, since the relative status of the former is likely to fall. A bad relationship can manifest itself in personality clashes and poor communication between the two departments.

Although we have emphasised the importance of market segmentation, it must be recognised that the potential of the technology is still advancing even if at a lower rate than previously. This means that from time to time the scope for incremental improvement becomes exhausted and an entirely new product incorporating the latest advances becomes essential. The ideal sequence is the development of a new product, its full exploitation through a series of incremental improvements, and its replacement by an entirely new product before it begins to lose market share. If new products are introduced too frequently there is insufficient time to capitalise on the investment made in the old. On the other hand, undue delay can result in the loss of market share; since the total market may still be expanding, the company in this situation may continue to experience a growth in sales volume which distracts attention from an erosion of its market share.

The key questions that management should address during this phase are:

- How can we utilise our technological competence to develop products for new market segments?
- How long can we expect to exploit existing products through incremental improvements?
- What is the optimum timing for introducing an entirely new product?
- What is happening to our market share?

Finally, as maturity approaches, a further re-orientation of the technical emphasis becomes necessary. Competitive products become more like commodities (e.g. detergents, motor oil), where it is almost impossible to establish a differential advantage by means of product performance. Where performance improvement is possible a considerable investment is required to obtain a marginal increment. In a perfect market all products

Table 3.1 Industry life cycle evolution and the business

Characteristic	Stage of life cycle		
	Early growth	Late growth	Maturity
Source of competitive advantage	New products	Improved or new products	Price
Rate of new product introduction	High	Medium	Very low
Product life	Very short	Medium	Long
Main technical focus	New technology in products	Products for defined market segments	Manufacturing processes Product durability and reliability
Relative importance of product cost	Low	Medium	Very high
Urgency of change	Very high	Medium	Low
Main determinant of business success	R&D	Marketing	Production and finance
Management style	Informal	Formalising	Highly formal

would be sold at the same price. Whilst this is not wholly true in practice, it is difficult to establish a substantial price differential between competing products. Thus profit becomes highly dependent upon the minimisation of cost. Technology contributes to this through improved manufacturing processes and formal management systems increasingly reliant upon IT. This is where the introduction of new technology into an ongoing activity can raise major difficulties. This concentration on the company's internal operations brings with it the danger of losing touch with the market. All too often mature companies give the impression that they are run more for the convenience of the managers than for service to the customer.

The argument so far parallels that in Chapter 2, particularly where a company is associated with one technology with which it has grown. The main features of this evolution are shown in Table 3.1.

Summarising the discussion so far one can see that management must consider:

- Where does our company lie on the industry–technology life cycle?
- Are the technological emphasis, the managerial systems and the influence of the functions appropriate to this stage of development?
- If not, how do we manage a reorientation?

Corporate regeneration

The progression up the life cycle appears as a natural sequence, with the slowing of technological growth associated with an increase in the degree of management formalisation as the company increases in size. However, as we saw in Chapter 1, the mature company is vulnerable to severe pressure on profit margins, the possible shrinkage of the total market, with an increase in product longevity, and the emergence of a new technology. It thus needs to develop an expertise in a new technology at a low point in the life cycle in order to support future organic growth. Movement in this direction is likely to appear unnatural and will be resisted. There is a strong inbuilt tendency to oppose and frustrate the style of management essential for the regeneration of the company. It appears to be a regression to an earlier period in the company's history which is now thought to have been unprofessional, chaotic, inefficient and wasteful.

Example: a European chemical company
Some years ago the author was invited to design an innovation programme for the board of directors of a division of a major European chemical company in a mature industry. When the company's own data were presented in a disguised form, purporting to relate to a competitor, there was unanimous agreement that the company faced a serious strategic gap; neither turnover nor RoI (return on investment) targets would be met. In

a long discussion a number of innovative proposals for the solution of that company's problems were put forward. The situation was transformed, however, when they were told that it was their own company they had been analysing. The gap which was so obvious to them previously was now rejected on the grounds that most of the gap resulted from pessimism in the forecasts they had made, and the current state of the economy. Minor operational improvements and the elimination of waste would enable them to close the gap without the need for innovation. Fortunately, an innovation programme instigated at the insistence of the company president helped to eliminate the shortfall in the contribution from its mature products which occurred a few years later.

The case of this European chemical company is typical of the managerial problems the authors have found in many companies in mature industries facing long-term decline. There are usually clear indications of the long-term trends, but the forecasts must be based on judgement to a large extent. Thus they lend themselves to a variety of interpretations by those who do not wish to see any changes introduced into a company which has achieved success in the past. But the need for a major strategic change must be based upon a view of the future, since it is usually too late to defer action until disaster strikes. There are many reasons why successful managers in the existing business may oppose change; these will be explored later. It can be seen that in a company of this type there are unlikely to be many internal entrepreneurs, and the stimulus for change is likely to come from top management. Frequently this is not forthcoming without a major corporate shake-up, often following a take-over.

In discussing the mature company it is easy to give an impression of incompetent, dead-wood management. This is not necessarily the case. Frequently these companies have been highly successful in the past and remain competitive within their sector of the market. Their skills have developed to manage an activity which is declining and they have no experience in managing change, which is seen as a threat to their personal strengths. In almost all the companies studied by the authors they have identified people who have a clear vision of what should be done; often they are at relatively low levels. Thus the potential for change exists; it just needs to be released.

R&D management are not immune to the resistance to change. They may well have lost their desire to innovate after what may have been a long period of relative stability. Thus innovation, which demands a change in attitudes and managerial style, may be difficult to achieve without the replacement of senior managers or the removal of new activities from their sphere of influence. Although we have discussed the problem from the viewpoint of management, it must not be forgotten that resistance extends to the workforce, where working practices have been established over many years. Proposals for change may be viewed as an attempt by management to remove hard-fought-for privileges. The changes themselves can cause genuine problems and stress to those who have become accustomed to regularity in their methods.

There are strong arguments for avoiding these problems and establishing the new activities on a green-field site (see Chapter 6). These are well exemplified by the relative ease with which Nissan were able to achieve high productivity from a new factory in an area without a tradition in the motor industry and with a workforce new to the industry. This is in marked contrast to the problems encountered by Ford in introducing new working practices in factories with a long tradition in motor manufacture. The main attractions of a green-field site are:

- the recruitment of managers with an entrepreneurial attitude appropriate to a situation of rapid change;
- the recruitment of a workforce free from the working practices developed in conditions of relative stability;
- the ability to install managerial control systems different from those in the rest of the organisation, thereby avoiding the jealousies and rivalries which occur where different management styles are in operation on the same site;
- the benefits of designing factory layout and equipment tailored to the needs of new technology.

The problems of introducing change into an existing organisation can be solved: that is what this book is about. Nevertheless, the difficulties must not be underestimated and the success rate is not encouraging. On the other hand, the success rate of green-field sites is much higher and their merits should be carefully considered, even when they may not appear to be attractive in comparison with introducing change into the existing organisation.

The multiproduct company

The previous section was written in the context of a company whose activities are concentrated on one product or a family of products closely related to one technology. There are, however, many diversified companies with a variety of products at different stages of the technology life cycle. In this situation there is a likelihood that the organisational pressures for conformity will lead to the sophisticated systems developed for the more mature parts of the company being imposed throughout. This can have a serious effect on the more innovative developments. The balance needs to be changed without detriment to the management of the more mature products. In general those companies which focus on providing an innovative environment whilst safeguarding the needs of the existing products have been able to maintain long-term corporate growth.

The company and its competition

Earlier it was noted that occasionally the emergence of a new technology introduces competition from an entirely new direction; this is sometimes referred to as innovation by invasion. Thus in order to maintain its market position a company needs to adopt the new technology. The difficulty in doing this should not be underrated and failures are more frequent than successes. This is illustrated by the experience of Avery in weighing machines. The company appreciated the need to move from mechanical designs to electronic, and allocated resources to the development of electronic systems. However, its lack of background in the technology resulted in slow progress, and little success was achieved until the company was taken over by GEC, which possessed the electronic expertise. Another classic case is that of the Swiss watch industry, which lost its mass market to Japanese electronic companies. The partial recovery of that industry, albeit from a smaller base, illustrates the point made earlier about changes in customer attribute preferences. Because of their time-keeping qualities, all electronic watches are sufficiently accurate for most users. Accuracy, the competitive advantage of the traditional Swiss watch, was an attribute of little relevance in the purchasing decision. Fashion design then became an important attribute which the Swiss were able to exploit with the Swatch.

Fortunately, for most of the time the competition is well defined and stable. The aim of the company must be to provide a product or service which is sufficiently attractive to gain it customer preference, and to develop products to maintain this competitive edge. It might be thought that the greater the performance advantage the stronger the competitive position. This is only partially true, and two other factors have to be carefully considered:

- The more ambitious the technical advance the higher the risk of failure to achieve the planned performance on time.
- Higher technical performance is likely to be reflected in higher product cost, at least initially.

It must not be forgotten that technical change involves doing something new to the company. The greater the change, the higher the uncertainty and its associated risk. Thus the aim must be to strike the optimum

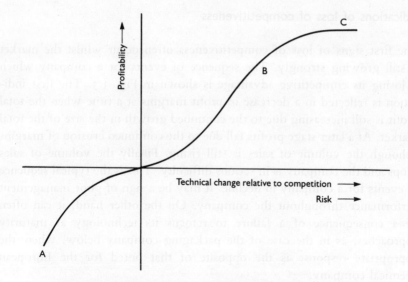

A Production obsolescence leads to loss of market share and profitability.
B Successful product innovation leads to increase in market share and profitability.
C Further technical advantage has little impact on market share and profitability,
  but risk continues to increase.

Fig. 3.2 Technical change relative to competition and its impact on profitability

balance between the degree of change, risk and profitability. In doing this
the anticipated actions of the competition must also be taken into account.
This is illustrated in Fig. 3.2. Where the degree of change is less than that
of the competition products will lose market share and profitability will
fall; this is the cost of doing nothing or very little. Where the degree of
technical change is greater than that introduced by the competition the
enhanced performance will yield a competitive advantage reflected in
increased market share and profitability. However, a point is reached
where any further improvement is likely to have only a limited impact
on market share or profitability, although the risk continues to rise.
Although Fig. 3.2 is only an illustration which it is almost impossible to
derive accurately, it does direct attention to four issues which should be
considered:

- What is the likely performance of competitive products?
- What is the expected performance over this time scale of our products
  as currently planned?
- How large a performance advantage should we aim to achieve?
- At what level of technical change will the risks become unacceptable
  in relation to possible market growth and profitability?

Indications of loss of competitiveness

The first signs of loss of competitiveness often occur whilst the market is still growing strongly. The sequence of events for a company which is losing its competitive advantage is shown in Fig. 3.3. The first indication is reflected in a decrease in profit margins at a time when the total profit is still increasing due to the continued growth in the size of the total market. At a later stage profits fall due to the continued erosion of margins although the volume of sales is still rising. Finally the volume of sales drops and the company is in serious difficulty. This is the typical sequence of events for a company in decline. It may be a sign of poor management performance throughout the company. On the other hand, it can often be a consequence of a failure to refocus its technology as maturity approaches, as in the case of the packaging company below, where the appropriate response is the opposite of that noted for the European chemical company.

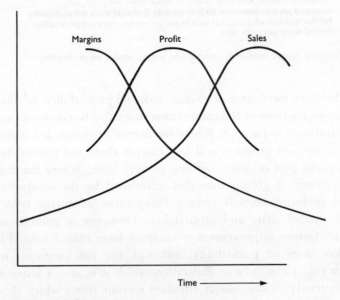

Fig. 3.3 Indicators of decline

Example: a materials packaging company
This company experienced a rapid growth in sales volume and profitability for many years based upon its R&D strength in a period of rapid development in its technology based upon the expertise of its founding entrepreneur and chairman. Thus the technical performance of its products provided its competitive advantage. It was characterised by

innovation, entrepreneurial management and informal systems. Its corporate plan envisaged a continuation of this growth in line with forecasts for the industry as a whole. However, examination of the financial performance revealed that its RoI had ceased to grow, although its sales volume was still increasing, albeit at a slower rate than previously. There were strong indications that the company's sales volume and RoI targets could not be achieved under the existing policies. No changes were introduced and the following five years saw no progress and a loss of market share. Major customers were lost to competitors on the basis of cost, although the total market continued to grow rapidly. The trends had been clear from an analysis of the financial data but the company had made no attempt to take corrective action. It had failed to appreciate that its traditional strengths in product innovation were of decreasing importance as the technology approached maturity. At this stage the technology was widely accessible and competitive advantage came from the application of managerial, technical and manufacturing skills to reduce the price of the product where it was almost impossible to establish a performance differential. Much of this failure could be attributed to the corporate culture founded on the technical and entrepreneurial orientation of the chairman.

The packaging company clearly exhibits the situation depicted in Fig. 3.3. Examination of a number of companies which have suffered from a decline indicates that the warning signals were usually there to be seen. The difficulty arises because at the time the changes are occurring the figures may lend themselves to a variety of interpretations. Other changes in the business environment can cloud the clarity of the data, in particular such factors as exchange rates and the growth of the economy as a whole. This provides management with external explanations for what is happening and distracts attention from the long-term implications of their own decisions. This may well be a valid argument but it behoves management to consider whether there may be other causes which are under their control, especially if their competitors do not appear to be suffering to the same extent. Where action is needed any delay increases the difficulty in rectifying the situation. Management should ask:

- What are the trends in our profit margins, profit, RoI and sales volume over a period of years?
- How do these compare with the performances of our main competitors?
- To what extent are unfavourable trends due to:
  (a) external factors outside our control;
  (b) managerial deficiencies;
  (c) the approach of market saturation;
  (d) the industry life cycle?
- Do they indicate the need to reorientate our technical focus?

Technical competitiveness

The establishment of a performance target to maintain a competitive advantage does not mean that the company has the skills to achieve it. This depends upon the ability of the technologists. Our consideration of the need for effective management of innovation must not blind us to the importance of the technical skills required. As with any resource, competent management can achieve little by itself.

Thus it is useful to assess both the technological strength of the company and the ability to deploy it effectively. What counts here is its position relative to the competition rather than some form of absolute measure. This can be done only by analysing critically past performance and assessing current capability. A matrix in the form shown in Fig. 3.4 can assist in presenting the results of this analysis in a visual form. It relates the current competitive strength of the firm to its portfolio of technologies which will be at different stages in their life cycles.

Any analysis of this type suffers from the shortcoming that it is a snapshot, and moreover, one based to a large extent on the subjective judgement of management. However, it does provide a basis for an informed discussion in its derivation. When done over a period of years it can also give an indication of the company's technological momentum in either a favourable or unfavourable direction. Furthermore, by drawing another matrix for the desired state at some time in the future it is possible to assess the 'technological gap', that is, an indication of where action is

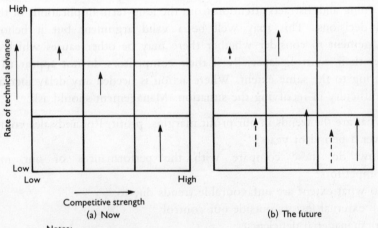

Notes:
1. The length of the line represents the relative size of the activity within the company's portfolio.
2. In the matrix for the future, - - - indicates the company's position without change, and —— indicates the desired position.

Fig. 3.4 Portfolio analysis of rate of technological progress *v.* competitive strength

needed in order to meet the technical strategic objectives (Fig. 3.4(b)). The situation as illustrated in this diagram is typical of what is often found by the authors, namely a desire for improvement across the board. Desirable though this may appear to be, it is unlikely to be achievable in practice. Choices have to be made about where best to deploy the limited resources available.

In arriving at the judgements necessary to complete the matrix there are a number of specific items that can be considered in relation to the competition. These include:

- the rate of R&D expenditure;
- average age of existing products;
- rate of introduction of new products;
- rate of change of market share;
- success rate in the introduction of new products;
- technical recruitment.

In order to assess these factors in relation to the competition it is essential to have a system of technical intelligence whereby the activities of the main competitors are closely monitored. A great deal of information is often available publicly which can give a good indication of how these companies are using their technology and the actions they are taking for the future. A common weakness is to assess competitors in relation to their current position rather than attempting to evaluate their plans for the future. Some companies have a long history of always being one step behind.

Technical change and finance

The validity of any decision for technical change must ultimately depend upon its contribution to the survival and profitability of the business. Thus there is an understandable desire to justify it in financial terms, often using similar criteria to those normally employed in evaluating a capital investment. This is difficult to do and does not necessarily lead to a correct decision, for a number of reasons we shall now discuss.

In a study of seven major Japanese companies the authors were surprised that there was little attempt to carry out any detailed financial evaluation, particularly for the more advanced technologies. However, a great deal of attention was devoted to technology forecasting and establishing detailed technical objectives, the achievement of which was financed irrespective of any short-term economic problems the firm might be facing. The technologists in these firms were given a high degree of discretion over what they should do to meet the objectives and were not expected to justify their actions in detailed financial terms. When we questioned this we were told that the uncertainties of innovation made financial justification meaningless and it was essential that funds were made available to meet long-term objectives whatever the cost. Only the technical directors could make the project decisions; that was what they were paid for. The companies were technology driven and a high proportion of their boards of directors had a technical background.

This Japanese approach is unlikely to be acceptable in the West, although it must be admitted that the companies interviewed were amongst the leaders in their industries worldwide. It does, however, raise the question of whether too much emphasis is placed upon financial aspects of innovation by many companies. This is not because this is undesirable but because it may not lead to the best decision.

What is the cost?

No programme for technical change would be embarked upon without estimates of both cost and duration. Objectives must be set and plans made for how they are to be achieved. However, since all change involves doing something which is new to the business, there will always be uncertainties. The more radical the technical change, the greater the uncertainty. Almost invariably these uncertainties manifest themselves as problems which require additional funds and involve delays. This results in modifications to the plans and possibly some amendment to the objectives. Planning there must be, but it must be realistic and flexible.

Examination of any company's experience of technical change will reveal that substantial cost escalation is the norm, frequently involving a final outcome several times greater than the original estimate. Some of this may be attributable to poor management of the project, but the major portion is likely to be the consequence of genuine uncertainties or the way in which the estimates were derived. An attitude of 'Yes, but it will be different this time', whilst commonplace, can only lead to self-delusion. It is to be hoped that it will be better this time, but it is unlikely to be substantially different.

Procedures to improve financial discipline within an organisation often exacerbate the difficulty. Let us examine briefly some scenarios of how cost estimates are derived. They will be initiated by the proposer of the change, who believes it to be desirable. His or her enthusiasm for it must be taken for granted, for without it the project would be unlikely to succeed anyway. The proposer will make an estimate of what is required in terms of tangible resources, equipment and manpower, which he or she will then translate into financial terms. Ideally this figure will be presented as his or her best estimate. In practice it is usually adjusted either upwards or downwards before presentation. The proposer might know from experience that there is always pressure to reduce the estimates. Therefore, in order to obtain the figure he or she believes to be necessary, he or she inflates the estimate in order to improve the likelihood of success with the funds he or she expects to be allocated. There are, however, circumstances in which a lower figure might be submitted if the proposer considers the original estimate too high for acceptance. The proposer works on the assumption that if he or she obtains sufficient resources to initiate it the company is committed; when further funds are required at a later date he or she assumes that they will have to be provided in order to save the investment already made. In these ways the establishment of the estimates loses touch with reality and becomes a matter of negotiation and game playing. Although undesirable, there are few companies where it does not occur to some degree. Nor must it be forgotten that the original best estimate can be expected to be optimistic.

There are no easy solutions to this dilemma, but management must appreciate that:

- The proposer believes in the project, and it is the decision-making environment, rather than a desire to deceive, which leads to these deceptions.
- Even in the absence of manipulation the estimates are likely to be optimistic.
- The viability of a proposal should not be highly sensitive to cost in-accuracies if it is to be supported.
- If accepted the funds necessary should be made available in spite of cost overruns unless there is new evidence to cause the viability of the project to be questioned.
- Financial restrictions which delay a change programme are likely to have a disproportionate impact on its profitability.
- If the above conditions cannot be satisfied the proposal should be rejected; if they are satisfied every effort should be made to bring it to a successful conclusion.

The extent to which these arguments apply is dependent upon the degree of innovation involved. In general they might be expected to be more relevant to radical innovations in the early stages of the life cycle. However, experience with new technology in both manufacturing processes and innovations in services in mature industries indicates the same difficulties, although in these situations it is usually possible to evaluate the benefits more accurately.

The questions which management should answer are:

- How inaccurate have the estimates been for the cost of similar changes in the past?
- To what extent have these inaccuracies been due to:
  (a) poor project management;
  (b) unforeseeable problems encountered;
  (c) the estimating and funding process?
- Are there sufficient funds available to support additional costs if necessary without a serious impact on cash flow?
- Is there a commitment to support the project to its conclusion notwithstanding development problems?
- Are there organisational barriers which inhibit the free flow of realistic information?

What are the benefits?

In the final analysis the benefit derived from a technical change programme will be reflected in the financial performance of the company. In theory it should be possible to relate the benefits directly to the associated costs in order to assess whether the change is financially viable. There are, however, a number of difficulties which will be experienced in practice.

Where the change relates to a new product or service the success depends upon its acceptance in the market, thereby generating a profit reflecting the price it can command compared with the cost of providing it. Thus there are two factors which must be considered: the size of the market and the cost of the product or service. Both of these can suffer from the same problems that beset the estimation of development cost. Frequently estimates of the size of the market are even more optimistic than those of development cost. There can never be an entirely satisfactory way to assess the size of the market for a new product or service. Nevertheless, it is possible to reduce some of the uncertainties by obtaining answers to the following questions:

- Will it satisfy a market need that cannot be met by current products? Frequently new technology first establishes itself in a price-insensitive specialist market where there is no alternative.
- Does it mark a significant improvement on existing products in relation to the attributes desired by the market? Market attributes were discussed earlier, particularly in relation to their change over time. A product meeting a combination of these desired attributes in a way not achievable with existing products will gain a competitive edge.

- Does it satisfy the market at a significantly lower price? It must be recognised that a fall in price per unit may reduce the total size of a saturated market when expressed in financial terms. However, the innovator is likely to counteract this by gaining a higher market share. It must also be assumed that the innovation will not be deferred indefinitely.

These questions are alternatives. If a satisfactory answer to one of them cannot be found the wisdom of proceeding with a radical new product must be questioned. In this situation an incremental improvement of existing products might be preferable. It should be noted that these questions are for consideration before the development is initiated. This is why significant improvements should be sought, not because they are essential for entering the market, but because the erosion of initial optimism as development progresses must be taken into account. If the attraction is marginal at the outset it is likely to have disappeared by the time development has been completed. It is not, of course, easy to quantify how significant 'significant' is, but the more radical the innovation, the greater the margin of safety required.

The criteria listed above might appear to be demanding. What is a company to do if none of its proposals can meet them? The answer is likely to lie more with the corporate attitude to innovation and creativity which inhibits the generation of potentially profitable proposals than with the rigour of the criteria. These aspects will be discussed in Chapter 5.

Profit is dependent upon the cost of providing the product or service after it has been developed. Usually these estimates also suffer from a degree of optimism. In a new product some of the difficulties experienced in development are likely to result in additional manufacturing cost. Poor design for production, an avoidable problem, is also a frequent cause of unnecessarily high manufacturing costs. It should be possible to estimate the benefits of a new manufacturing process or a managerial system to a high degree of accuracy. The errors which are often found in practice stem from an unrealistic assessment of the operating conditions. For example, the investment in new equipment may be justified on a utilisation rate which the machine is theoretically capable of meeting, but which the market demand patterns of the company are unlikely to support. Assuming that the prices charged are what the market will bear, any increase in unit cost reflects directly on profit, thereby reducing the benefit obtainable from the innovation.

In the discussion so far we have suggested that a technical change should be evaluated in relation to the additional benefit to be derived from the financial investment. This implies that the status quo will be preserved in the absence of innovation. Rarely is this the case, for the actions of competitors cannot be ignored. Their innovations move the goal posts. Thus it is necessary to ask: 'What is the cost of not innovating?'.

The real benefit from an innovation is the additional profit it generates plus the loss of profit which would be incurred without it. All too often this is ignored in the evaluation of a technical change. It is analogous to the cost of essential maintenance, which is unavoidable. When viewed in this way the justification for a change is enhanced even though the net benefit may not meet the company's normal investment criteria.

Notwithstanding what we have said about the evaluation process, it must be recognised that most companies carry out some form of financial justification comparable to that used in assessing a capital investment. What we have stressed is the need for realism and the focusing of attention on the marketplace from which the benefits must flow in the long run. Risk is unavoidable, but a technical innovation which appears to have the ingredients for market success should be supported, provided there are sufficient finances to enable it to be brought to a conclusion. The most common causes of failure are:

- unforeseeable difficulties; these are a reflection of the inherent un-certainties and are to a great extent unavoidable;
- the initiation of projects where the benefits, if successful, are marginal;
- lack of urgency in development through financial restrictions or managerial failings which surrender the benefits of a successful in-novation to a competitor;
- the initiation of projects where the company does not have the cash resources to support cost escalations (e.g. Rolls-Royce RB 211).

Technical change and the experience curve

The experience curve represents the fall in the unit cost of a product with the increase of cumulative production (Fig. 3.5). It is a consequence of incremental product development, improvement in manufacturing processes and managerial learning. This phenomenon was first noted in the production costs of Dakota aircraft during the war and has since been found to apply in a wide range of both consumer and industrial products. It has also been noted in some service operations although less research has been conducted in this area. Typically it is a 70–80 per cent curve: every time the cumulative production volume doubles the unit cost falls to that proportion of what it was previously.

This relationship has a number of important implications which must be taken into account when planning the introduction of a technical change, namely:

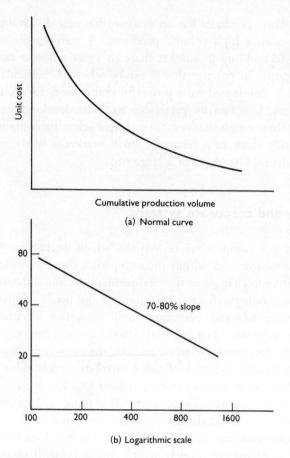

(a) Normal curve

(b) Logarithmic scale

Fig. 3.5 The experience curve

- The initial unit cost will be high and is likely to be greater than that of products incorporating the existing technology, even though it will eventually fall below it. Thus the innovator must:
  (a) seek applications for which the product will be bought for its performance attributes where price is not the major consideration (it has been noted earlier that these are likely to be relatively small, specialist markets); *or*
  (b) accept that it must be priced below the production cost initially in order to establish itself in the market; this effectively means an addition to the development cost.
- An evaluation of the project which compares the cost at introduction with the production cost of the existing product gives an unfavourable comparison which can result in the rejection of the innovation if the future experience curve gains are not taken into account explicitly.

- A small-volume producer has an unavoidable cost disadvantage when competing with a high-volume producer. A considerable investment is required to build up its market share to a size where it can compete on equal terms. In practice this is rarely achieved, particularly where the market is dominated by a powerful competitor, for example IBM in computers. It is usually preferable to focus development on niche markets in these circumstances, for example scientific computers. Thus a high market share of a relatively small market is likely to be more profitable than a low share of a large one.

Technology and corporate systems

Any business is a complex set of systems which interact both with the external environment and within the company. Thus strategic decisions must be sensitive to changes in the environment, technical decisions to the advances in technology, finance decisions to the needs of investors and financial institutions, and operations and marketing decisions to the consumer, and so on. The internal activities are often considered in relation to the functional departments, but the resources they deal with – technology, people, materials, finance, markets – cross these functional boundaries. This web of relationships is held together by a hierarchy of objectives, to give coherence to operational actions, and the information system, to supply the mechanism for the transmission of control and decision-making information. Other elements can be added to this model. There are also alternative models which might be used to describe the functioning of a business.

Whichever way one chooses to look at a business organisation there is one inescapable fact: the relationships are complex and a change introduced into one part is likely to have ramifications in other parts of the systems. However, in order to enable the whole to function effectively it has to be broken down into elements to make it more manageable. There is a division of responsibility and tasks are assembled into units combining people with similar roles, skills or knowledge. This we recognise as the traditional functional or hierarchical organisation. This is necessary to simplify the operational functioning of the whole. It is likely to work most effectively in conditions of relative stability. But it can fail disastrously when a change is introduced in one part of the system without due consideration of its impact throughout all the internal systems and, sometimes, the external as well. There are thus a number of characteristics of a technical change which must be considered:

- the impact on all the corporate systems;
- the ability of the existing organisational structure and systems to handle the impact without modification;
- the increased flow of communication within the systems and across boundaries necessary when introducing change;
- the need for a rapid response time to enable the assimilation of new information and managerial action without delay.

All these aspects will be discussed at length in later chapters. They will lead to five general conclusions:

(a) It may be necessary to modify the organisational structure or introduce a new one to facilitate the change process.
(b) No organisational structure can in itself provide more than a general facilitating framework.
(c) Within that framework success depends upon the actions of individuals who alone can appreciate the wider implications of the totality of the change.
(d) Some form of project management is essential in order to focus on the imperatives of the change programme.
(e) The role of top management is critical. They must ensure the achievement of the programme objectives, but within a control system which provides the project manager with a minimum of operational constraints.

The hierarchy of objectives

It is possible, and indeed desirable, for a coherent hierarchy of objectives to be established, thereby ensuring that all actions are aligned to the objectives of the business. Departmental objectives should be set to achieve the corporate objectives and similarly down throughout the company as far as the level of the individual. This process is not easy to attain in practice. In many cases it can be counterproductive, where insufficient care is taken in formulating them in relation to the effect they have on the actions taken to implement them. For example, the maximisation of sales volume for marketing and the minimisation of unit cost for production provide easily understood objectives for the two departments. Neither may be consistent with the business objective of profit maximisation, nor may it be possible to achieve both at the same time; thus this may lead to interfunctional conflict. Although this is an obvious example, there are many others where the implications are more subtle.

Departments also have their own objectives, although they are usually implicit. These are usually related to their desire to achieve or maintain power or status within the company. In recent years this has often manifested itself in the attitudes and actions of many data-processing departments, which have a vested interest in the maintenance of their position at the centre of the company's information system. With the advent of microcomputers this position is threatened. It is not surprising, therefore, that we have observed in many companies a strong resistance by these departments to the introduction of the new technology. It is a genuine threat to them and is understandable, although it is undesirable from the corporate viewpoint.

Individuals also have their personal objectives which are more important to them than the greater good of the company. Where a technical change appears to threaten these personal interests they will resist it. This form of opposition is often thought to be confined to the lower levels of the organisation, where it can take a highly visible form, for example strike action. However, there is now a growing volume of research findings to indicate that managerial resistance is more likely to be the major barrier to technical change.

Frequently the objectives of a technical change have been found to lack clarity or to become modified as they permeate down through the organisation. Voss,[1] in his research into the introduction of advanced manufacturing technology, reports that the corporate objectives for approving the investment are frequently expressed in relation to aims, often difficult to quantify, such as quality or responsiveness to the market, whereas those implementing the system have cost minimisation or output maximisation as their objectives. This mismatch can lead to the system failing to achieve its business objectives.

The technical system

The technical system can be considered at two levels. First there is the innovation chain covering R&D, the design of the product or process and its implementation in production. Secondly, there is the flow of materials and operations on them, extending from purchasing through manufacture to marketing. Both these chains cross functional boundaries.

It is beyond the scope of this book to examine the many problems which are commonplace when each aspect of the flow is considered in isolation within one department. All too often a host of difficulties are encountered when a new product is transferred from design to production. It may be expensive, or in some cases impossible to manufacture. It may be incompatible with the existing manufacturing equipment, as, for example, when the material is changed. Manufacturing processes may be designed so that they cannot accommodate design changes, as occurred in one large company which was unable to transfer to metric product sizes without major modifications to a recently installed new plant.

Often these problems arise because a technical change is introduced to solve a difficulty in one part of the technical system without consideration of its effect upon the system as a whole. It is analogous to the road improvement scheme which removes one bottleneck only to create another. Often on examination it transpires that within the company there is nobody responsible for the total system.

The technical and human systems

This is the major cause of difficulties in the introduction of technical change and will be examined in detail in later chapters. A few examples will be cited here to illustrate ways in which such difficulties can occur.

The QWERTY typewriter keyboard was designed in the nineteenth century with the purpose of limiting the speed of typists, who otherwise would have jammed the mechanical keys. Although this technical limitation no longer applies and many preferable layouts have been designed, they have not been adopted because of the difficulty, if not impossibility, of retraining typists experienced in the traditional layout.

Many technical systems are designed without taking into account the needs or skills of the operators. Often the designers have no experience in operating the equipment themselves, as with the tractor manufacturer which produced a cab design with poor rear vision, an essential feature for farmers, who need to position their tools accurately. This is also seen in many computer applications. The use of the term 'user friendly' is revealing, in that it implies that many systems, not only in computers, are frequently user unfriendly.

An unforeseen result of the introduction of automatic teller machines by banks was that the banks failed to appreciate the effect these would have on the total business through the lack of personal contact between the customer and the company. A technical system was installed in isolation from its impact upon the market.

In one electronics company quality control was removed from a central quality control department to the operatives, who were capable of detecting faulty components. The payment system, however, remained unchanged, and related to the volume of their output and not to its quality. Thus the introduction of the new system, which meant that they were no longer paid for rejected items, effectively reduced their pay. It is not surprising that the change resulted in industrial relations difficulties. The technical change had been implemented without an understanding of how a non-technical system, payment, would affect the response of those responsible for operating it.

Summary

In this section we have touched upon some of the problems of introducing a specific technical change into an organisation. Essential features for success are:

- The objectives of the change programme must be directly related to the business objectives.
- The implementation of the change must be planned in relation to all the internal systems which will be affected by it.
- Areas of potential conflict with established procedures and existing departmental and personal interests must be identified.
- One person or a team of people covering all the systems affected and crossing traditional functional boundaries must be appointed.

Reference

1. Voss, C. A. (1986) Implementing manufacturing technology: a manufacturing strategy approach. *International Journal of Operations and Production Management*, **6**(4), (*special edition*: 'Operations Management in the 1990s').

4 The organisational implications of successful technological change

Successful technological change is dependent on two principal factors: the technology itself, its form, appropriateness and application; and the ability of the organisation and the people within it to grasp the technical opportunity and translate a technological success into a business success. The technology part is complex enough, but many will argue that it is the change of the organisation itself and the behaviour of those within it which is the more complex and crucial to the successful exploitation of technology (Fig. 4.1). This chapter addresses the changes in organisation and behaviour which are most often required. Chapters 6 and 7 go on to address the issue of how we can achieve these changes.

The areas we shall look at are:

- organisation structure and design;
- organisation structure, company strategic style and technology investment;
- skill and labour demands;
- employment patterns;
- recruitment and selection;
- pay structure and pay design;

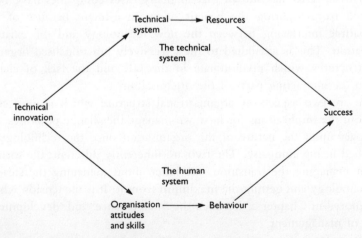

Fig. 4.1 The path to the successful implementation of technology

- employee involvement;
- suggestion schemes;
- quality circles;
- people systems;
- the trade union response.

Organisation structure and design

Organisation structures usually represent or certainly come in time to represent power structures. The electric valve company which placed its electronics development project under the general manager for valves clearly did not see how threatening the new technology could become to his existing power base. The technology was developed but not exploited by this company. Similarly, the R&D department of a now successful British engineering company described to the authors how one of their most successful recent innovations survived because it did not threaten the products of any of the group's constituent companies. The product is now manufactured in both the UK and Japan as a joint-venture operation, as none of the group's companies was able or willing to run with the venture.

Successful technological change will threaten the existing order. Those who have made their name and reputation on today's order are not likely to be too happy about competing for success in the new order. These somewhat crude considerations of power are important if we are to understand the fundamental implications of technological change.

A recent study of the introduction of advanced manufacturing technology in the UK[1] has shown that in many cases companies have been prevented from securing the benefit of an investment because of the incompatible interfacing between the new technology and the existing organisation. This is attributed to the excessively functionalised organisation structures which predominate in the UK and the lack of clarity between the interacting parts of the organisation.

There are two aspects of organisational structure which require consideration: the implications for how we manage the change processes and the impact upon the nature of the organisation once the technology is established in the company. The two are inherently different: the former is about managing the transition, the latter about managing the steady-state technology and getting the maximum from it. It is the tension which was explored in Chapter 2, between the 'maintenance' and 'development' aspects of management.

Traditional organisation structures have largely been designed around

Fig. 4.2 A functional or segmented organisation structure

particular functions, the belief being that in this way efficiency is maximised, responsibilities are clear and control can be centralised (Fig. 4.2).

Such structures arise from views of scientific management and rest
heavily upon the assumption that the organisation's future activities can
be predicted with a high degree of certainty. This is rarely the case in
managing technological innovation. The problems are complex and cross
the functional boundaries. Furthermore, age, experience and seniority in
the organisation (the traditional status measures) may have little relevance
to solving these complex problems.

In a range of different ways organisations are moving towards multifunctional group working structures. Under the names of task teams or
project teams, these provide an alternative mode of managing technological change. Those organisations in which this form of working has
become the norm are much better able to grasp the challenges of technological change.

Example

A major manufacturing company, whilst introducing advanced manufacturing systems to
support a new product range, created two parallel structures, one for maintaining the
existing production and the other for managing the new processes and equipment (Fig.
4.3). The existing products were organised around mini-factories or mini-plants where the
manager of each was fully accountable for production, cost, engineering, people and
quality. The advanced manufacturing systems were managed by the parallel structure
headed by the strategy committee. Each of the subcommittees had responsibility for a
major part of the technology change and had on it members from each of the departments affected by the change.

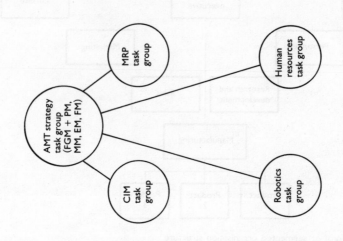

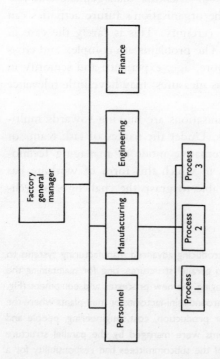

Fig. 4.3 Organising technological change alongside production

Using this example we can see how the two sides of the organisation structure carry out the maintenance and development roles. The key issues for managers adopting these hybrid organisational structures are:

- ensuring the right balance of resources between the two structures;
- deciding whether the task teams should be staffed primarily by full-time or part-time members;
- bearing in mind that individuals cannot be expected to undertake a full-time 'line' job as well as participate fully in a task team;
- recognising that there will be tension between the two structures, and managing this accordingly.

The organisation structure of the 'steady-state' part of the organisation is also likely to change as a result of the introduction of new technology systems. This is particularly true with the introduction of ever more sophisticated information technology which has been designed to give management much better decision support. The problem is, however, that many of these IT strategies reflect a top-down view of management which supports a centralised decision-making structure. This very easily can have the effect of choking off the responsiveness and flexibility which is the fundamental prerequisite of effective task teams. Furthermore, in highly automated process lines we often encourage the operators to contribute to incremental improvement, which can only have meaning if appropriate information is given at this level, so that informed local decisions can be made. Too many IT strategies leave operators and supervisors quite bewildered and devoid of relevant information.

Example
When BMW built their new factory in Regensburg to build the new 3 series, they adopted an integrated approach to the new organisation structure, information strategy, and office layout. The organisation is based on production centres giving the manager a planned set of data on functions within his control. The information system has also been designed to support project teams in the research and engineering centre as well as in the factory itself. Office and communications support is integrated around the managerial ethos of the plant and the design of the production process itself.

The organisation structure of an innovative organisation can and should be designed interactively with the technology itself, the information and communications systems and the desired managerial ethos. None of these three should be seen in a wholly deterministic way. As we have seen, we do have technological choice, and systems and processes can reflect the organisational structure we want and our style of management. Equally, the organisation and the information systems need to reflect the techno-logical requirements, and so on.

When new technology is introduced into an existing organisation we need to explore further the effect that technology itself can have upon the organisation once implemented, that is, the extent to which the introduction of technology within the organisation, in the form of information or process technology, of itself changes the decision-making structure of that organisation. In other words, does an integrated management information system necessarily lead to a greater concentration of power at the top of the organisation or can it be used to facilitate the devolution of decision making further down the hierarchy?

Example

In a recent discussion the technical director of an electronics company demonstrated how the terminal on his desk could call up the current working of each person in the design team three layers below him in the corporate hierarchy. He was proud of his ability to intervene at this level, as he would now be able to examine and control work activity more closely. Such examples raise some interesting questions as to how this director sees his role and that of the three layers of management beneath him. The danger is that, as information systems become more integrated and cross-functional, the shape of the organisation and individual job requirements can become predetermined by those who have the responsibility for designing these systems. This can of itself introduce a new form of rigidity in the organisation which makes it less flexible and less able to adapt. The introduction of early forms of materials requirements planning systems in manufacturing environments appears to have had this effect.

One company in the USA became so concerned at the ability of senior management to 'leapfrog' the decision-making structure that they placed a mandatory four-hour delay between information being received and its being accessible to senior management. The idea behind this was that middle management is employed to solve problems and should be given a reasonable chance to do so. The Ford Motor Company insist that senior management know immediately any production line stops. It must be difficult for middle management in this situation to feel that they are given much of an opportunity to resolve such problems.

We can say, however, that the application of new technology, and in particular information technology, within businesses will have the following impacts on the organisation:

- flatter organisational structures;
- the creation of multifunctional teams to plan and manage change;
- much greater flexibility within teams and between teams;
- authority based on what you contribute rather than on the position you hold (the shift from positional to sapiential power);
- accountability clearly at the point of production or service (as technology becomes more complex it becomes too easy to push accountability elsewhere 'the computer again');

- constant discussion and incremental improvement through joint problem-solving and creativity teams.

Organisation structure, company strategic style and technology investment

A common theme running through the chapters of this book is the overall approach organisations take to managing their business. What balance do organisations make between the short-term and the long-term goals? Is it left to the corporate centre to devise the overall investment strategy or is it up to operating companies to develop their own strategies for corporate approval? Is the company measured and controlled by its contribution to a wide range of corporate goals or merely by the achievement of a series of financial targets set for each company irrespective of whether or not long-term investment is contemplated? Goold and Campbell,[2] in their study of corporate styles, conclude that the answers to these questions do have implications for the successful management of technological change.

They concentrate their study on three main types of organisation. The strategic planning companies are those which push for maximum competitive advantage in the businesses in their portfolio. They seek to build their portfolios around a small number of core businesses. In pursuing these goals of pre-eminence in the core areas they are often prepared to make long-term investments to achieve or further their supremacy in the business area. Investment in product or process technology which supports these strategic goals is carefully considered and is often accepted even if the payback is over a relatively long period. Companies studied were BOC, BP, Cadbury Schweppes, Lex, STC and United Biscuits.

The financial control companies are those seen as focusing on financial performance rather than competitive position. They expand through acquisition rather than through organic growth. 'High technology' is acquired through 'high tech' companies rather than through being concerned with actively managing major technological change. Businesses which fail to meet the financial criteria are disposed of rather than invested in and turned around. Whilst the financial performance of these companies is undoubtedly good, this has largely been at the expense of long-term organic business building. Companies adopting this style included BTR, Hanson, Ferranti, GEC and Tarmac.

The strategic control companies balance competitive and financial ambitions. They support growth in strategically sound, profitable businesses but rationalise their portfolios in much the same way as the financial

Table 4.1   The influence of corporate strategy on an organisation's propensity to invest in advanced technology. Developed from Goold and Campbell (1987).

Strategic planning	Strategic control	Financial control
Pursue major investments in core areas	Develop successful areas incrementally	Seek high margins and opportunities for profit growth
Investment in technology which supports core	Investment in technology which supports successful areas	Avoids long payback investments
Will accept high-risk product and process technology	Will accept balanced product and process technology risk	Avoids technology risk
Push for maximum competitive position	Balance competitive position with financial ambitions	Stretch for financial position

control companies. The style permits businesses to adopt long-term strategies and they will often be prepared to consider and invest in fundamental technological change. Examples include Courtaulds, ICI, Plessey and Vickers.

If we build upon this classification then we can start to summarise how these three different types of corporate strategy are likely to have an impact upon an organisation's propensity to invest in technological change (Table 4.1).

The distribution of technology spend across these three types is also likely to be different. For example, where the financial control company wishes to improve performance and productivity there are often high levels of investment in information technology such as financial and production control systems, which are often presented as short-payback investments. The strategic planning company is more likely to invest in the long-term development of its core business, even if the payback is a long way off. Pilkington's development of the float glass process is a good example of the long-term technological investment of a strategic planning company.

The study of the competitiveness of the UK's electronics sector[3] vividly reinforces the need to adopt appropriate organisational structures if industry is to become world competitive. It observes that many of the UK's electronics companies have become highly decentralised operating to a financial planning model. It concludes: '. . . decentralization to small units has limited the scale and ambition to that of the units rather than the company as a whole. Numbers driven rather than issues driven planning has reinforced a focus on shorter term results rather than longer term investment to create major new businesses.' It goes on to say that the limited role which the corporate centre has played in many of these companies has not redressed the short-term and numbers-driven orientation of the operating units.

The key lesson which emerges is that in every respect technology change is a process of application which embodies choice. We may not recognise the choices we have to make and allow others to make them for us, and thereby perhaps weaken our business. Packaged management information systems embody assumptions about how organisations wish to make decisions and, indeed, about which decisions they should make. It therefore becomes the responsibility of senior management to decide in advance the nature of the organisation which they require and to demand that the decision support system is designed to fit it rather than the other way round.

Skill and labour demands

Attempts have been made to determine the precise impact of technological change upon skill and labour demands. General trends are difficult to find and even where they exist they do not tell us much that is of direct help in understanding the implications for our own companies. Technology applications are highly diffuse and difficult to categorise. What is of immense importance, and is often ignored, is the increased choice which the introduction of new technologies brings to the organisation. For example, a recent study[4] of the use of advanced computer-controlled machine tools in West Germany and the UK highlighted the differences in how they were applied and utilised in an organisational sense. In the UK, on equivalent equipment making similar products, the tendency was largely to separate machine programming from operation. In contrast, the West German companies tended to increase the skill levels through combining the two tasks. It is this fundamental level of choice which is so often overlooked, and simplistic conclusions which state that AMT will automatically deskill work for all but a few tend to blur and confuse rather than to help the practising manager.

The authors' experience in studying both the Japanese and the West German experience of technological change reinforces the view that it is the adaptability of skill which is important rather than the historical pattern. There are few innovations which have no impact upon the skills and behaviour of people in the organisation. It is not the intention here to discuss relative increases or decreases in skill demands, but rather the propensity of organisations to change their skill base. It is undoubtedly the case that those organisations which have invested heavily in changing their skill base have prospered most when requiring major change.

Some of the examples are unexpected. The British Steel Corporation has been quietly changing its skill base. Not only have old restrictions on

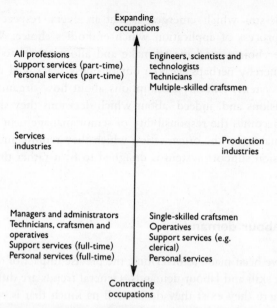

Fig. 4.4 The changing occupational balance (Institute of Manpower Studies)

skill demarcations now been largely removed, but every individual is offered the opportunity of constant skill development. The idea of the learning company is one where all levels of employees have opportunities to better themselves through skill enhancement. Developing such a culture may in the short term over-extend the skill base for the current requirements, but in the long term a workforce is created which is *used* to learning and for whom adaptability becomes the norm.

We can predict the overall trends in the broad occupational categories (Fig. 4.4). In those industries most susceptible to new technology (manufacturing, information and process) the trend will be towards higher and broader rather than lower levels of skills. But the trends are by no means uniform, and can give counter-indications. A Swedish study compared the skills and tasks involved in successive stages of the automation and computerisation of machine tools (Table 4.2) and suggested that the operative role was becoming less skilled. If, however, we were to look at the totality of the tasks (planning, programming, maintenance and problem solving), then the result would be reversed. We therefore have to look at the totality of tasks and their potential redistribution, rather than see skill changes from the perspective of current jobs.

If we look at manufacturing in the UK we can see (Fig. 4.5) a dramatic reduction in overall levels of employment coupled with an equally dramatic shift in the distribution of the types of job required to be performed.

Table 4.2   The impact of successive stages of numerical control on operator skills (Elsasser, Sweden)

Operation	CI	C2	NCI	NC2	NC3
Planning					
Choice of tools	X				
Choice of cutting data	X				
Setting up	X		X		
Adjust cutting data	X		X		
Machine operation	X	X	X	X	X
Load/unload	X	X	X	X	X
Measure/control	X	X	X	X	
	Skilled	Semi-skilled	Skilled	Semi-skilled	Unskilled

CI   = Conventional machine
C2   = Automation without NC
NCI = NC without setters
NC2 = NC with setters
NC3 = NC with setters and auto measuring
X   = Performed by machine operator

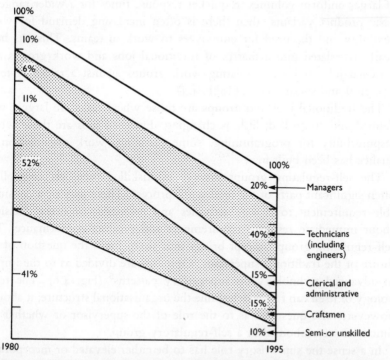

Fig. 4.5 Projected changes in the volume and occupational structure of employment in the UK manufacturing industry, 1980 and 1995. *Source*: Commission of the European Communities (in association with the journal *Futures*) (1984) Eurofutures: the challenges of innovation. *The FAST Report*, p. 100. Butterworths.

Table 4.3 The design of work, technology and the environment

	Factors									
	Technical interdependence		Technical uncertainty		Environmental dynamics		Growth needs		Social needs	
Work designs	Low	High	Low	High	Low	High	Low	High	Low	High
Traditional jobs	×		×		×		×		×	
Traditional work groups		×	×		×		×			×
Enriched jobs	×			×		×		×	×	
Self-regulating work groups		×		×		×		×		×

Source: Nadler, G. and Robinson G. (1987) Planning, designing and implementing advanced manufacturing technology. In Wall, T. (eds.) *The Human Side of Advanced Manufacturing Technology*, Wiley.

If the adoption of technology is also accompanied, as it so often is, by the need to move away from production and service patterns which are of large, uniform volumes to quicker response times for a wider range of basic product variants, then there is often increasing demand for work flexibility and the need for employees to work in teams. This has been neatly translated into a matrix of traditional jobs and work groups and enriched jobs and self-regulating work groups against a range of technological and social factors (Table 4.3).

The traditional jobs and groups are those where tasks are largely well defined and controlled; little is changing. Enriched jobs are those where responsibility for programming, some planning, work organisation or quality has been built in.

The self-regulating groups involve multiskilled members controlling often significant parts of the total work process. There may be a considerable requirement to change activities and priorities, or make decisions about immediate resource requirements and product conformance. The self-regulating group concept brings into sharp focus the question of the future of the traditional supervisor. Opinions are divided as to the impact of advanced technology on supervisory patterns[5] (Fig. 4.6). The technology of itself can rarely determine the organisational structure; it should, however, raise questions as to the role of the supervisor or whether the functions are embodied in a self-regulatory group.

In a sense the supervisory role has to be either elevated or incorporated into the flexible team as a team leader. Fig. 4.6 gives examples of the two principal options. They do not represent fundamental differences but different emphases to suit different operational requirements.

Technical uncertainty is decreasing as information and decision support

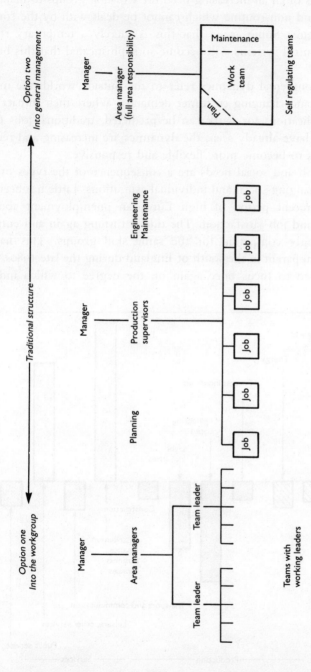

Fig. 4.6 Supervisory role options

systems take routine decisions away from working groups. On the other hand, there is often an increasing need for working groups to manage the unforeseen and non-routine which cannot be dealt with by the computer control systems. Some argue that this is merely a temporary state, as computer control systems will become so sophisticated that this becomes unnecessary.

The environmental dynamics refer to the outside world: the markets, competitors and changing customer demands. Where their impact is low and the implications for work can be predicted, traditional jobs tend to stay. As we have already seen, the dynamics are increasing and requiring organisations to become more flexible and responsive.

The growth and social needs are a consequence of the types of job as well as of changing social and individual aspirations. Little has been heard during the recent period of high European unemployment about job enrichment and job satisfaction. The tide is turning again and employers are increasingly competing for the same skill groups. This has been particularly apparent in the south of England during the late 1980s. Attention will need to focus once again on the degree to which individual

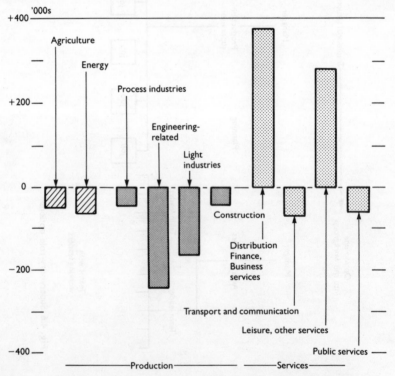

Fig. 4.7 Sectorial changes in the UK workforce, 1985–90. *Source:* Institute of Manpower Studies.

opportunity for growth and broader social needs will have to be incorporated into job design. As we have seen, the effective use of advanced technology will in many areas demand greater flexibility and skill, which in turn will provide for the growth and social demands of those employed in these jobs.

If we now turn to the overall levels of labour demand we can see that there are fundamental shifts occurring in the distribution of the workforce across the economy (Fig. 4.7). Manufacturing will continue to decline in terms of employment in the UK, with the service industries seeing considerable expansion. Even in those manufacturing sectors where expansion is still occurring, the increasing application of advanced technology does not guarantee consequential increases in employment.

Figures 4.8 and 4.9 show increases in output against employment in the telecommunications and electronics industries in the UK. The same pattern appears to be emerging in the embryonic biotechnology industry.[6]

One further factor which is becoming strongly apparent in all the major economies of Western Europe is the dramatic fall in the number of school leavers as the baby boom of the 1960s works its way through the decades. The traditional company response to the introduction of new technology is the recruitment of entrants to the labour market to work in the new processes as an alternative to retraining. The demographic situation will require companies to consider much more closely than hitherto retraining

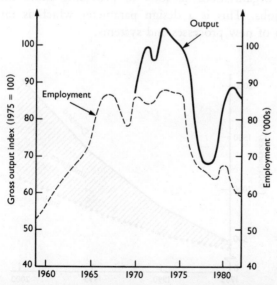

Fig. 4.8 Gross output and the effect on employment in telecommunications. *Source*: Luc Soete (ed.) (1985) *Technological Trends and Employment 3. Electronics and Communications*, Gower, p. 117.

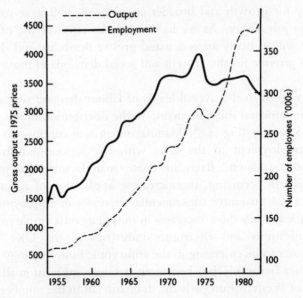

Fig. 4.9 Output and the effect on employment in electronics. *Source*: Luc Soete (ed.) (1985) *Technological Trends and Employment 3. Electronics and Communication*, Gower, p. 3.

rather than recruitment to service the requirements of new products and processes. The evidence suggests that skills will be in short supply, which will require organisations to look to providing more interesting and stimulating jobs. This is a design parameter which is rarely included in the design of new processes and systems.

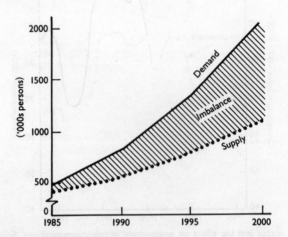

Fig. 4.10 The project shortfall in the supply of software engineers in Japan. *Source*: MITI (1988) Reproduced in *Performance and Competitive Success*, NEDO 1988.

Even Japan, with its far greater output of technical graduates than Western Europe per head of population, is predicting major skill shortages in key areas (Fig. 4.10).

Employment patterns

Accelerating technological change presents some fascinating implications for the pattern of employment for the technologists themselves as well as for those directly affected by the impact of the technology upon the organisation. Let us first of all consider the technologists.

By the technologists we refer to those who have the understanding of the technology and the drive and skill to make it work. Such people have often felt neglected within many of our large organisations. Those who have had a combination of drive and frustration have often left to set up their own businesses either entirely separate from their original company or, in the more enlightened corporations, under the guidance of the parent company. A study by Ed Roberts of the Massachusetts Institute of Technology's Sloan School of Management showed that of 39 innovators who left one company in the USA after five years, 85 per cent of their businesses were flourishing, and these businesses had between them a combined turnover of 2.5 times that of the companies from which they had all come! This may not be typical across all industries, but it seems to be borne out in those sectors which are the greatest potential users of technology. If we have such creative talent within our organisations why don't we have the means of exploiting it rather than allowing it to dissipate through frustration?

The norms, values and culture which suit the innovator rarely suit the operations manager wanting to increase efficiency and production:

Innovator	Operations
autonomy	control
flexibility	discipline
few deadlines	multiple, tight deadlines
thinking	reacting
experimenting	conforming
creating	problem solving

R&D functions are often not situated on the manufacturing site. This is no coincidence: the cultures of the two have to be so different. Entrepreneurship is best separated from the ongoing routine of the organisation; its constant crises call for short-term solutions. The disadvantage of this separation is that once we transfer technology from the one to the other, the cultural gap can be so large that the transfer is not effective (see p. 38). This is the challenge for managing the change process.

Derek Hornby, chairman of Rank Xerox, sees entrepreneurs as often troublesome people who do not fit easily into a corporate role: 'We find it much better to fund them to do their own thing and take a piece of the action'. This can be seen as a high-risk strategy by some chief executives, but innovation is risky, and to allow the innovators to have control over their own satellite company can reduce the internal risk of the corporate machine stifling the idiosyncratic ways of the typical innovator.

Employment patterns for innovative organisations may well include some form of networking, self-employment or venture companies being set up under the auspices of the parent company.

Example

Rank Xerox have set up a well-established and now well-publicised networking system with some of their professional staff. These people are self-employed and contract their services to the company. They are free to take on work for other companies and can undertake their work in whatever way they choose as long as it meets the company's specification.

The successful company needs both good innovators and good operations personnel. We therefore have to achieve a difficult balance when establishing employment patterns, as we need to retain key staff of both types for whom very different patterns may apply.

The second consideration is the employment patterns of employees affected by technological change. The impact can be wide and diverse. The move to a core workforce coupled with a greater proportion of staff on a temporary or part-time basis is commonly portrayed as being a result of technological change. The extent of this practice can certainly be put down to the need for increasing market responsiveness and flexibility, but it is difficult to say whether this is due to the impact of technology *per se*. New capital investment of whatever sort brings with it the need to optimise the investment, which may require a more numerically flexible workforce. If we turn to skill flexibility, then we can perhaps see a different set of demands being placed especially on key employees. The increasing complexity of technology itself brings closer to the fore the tension between on the one hand requiring ever more sophisticated and specialist skills to understand the technology's application and on the other hand the need for employees to integrate the technology into the rest of the product or process; this requires more general and integrative skills among managerial and technical grades.

Wild[7] has researched the idea that as process technology becomes more and more integrated and complex, the traditional managerial job of progress chasing, crisis management and breakdown problem solving becomes diluted as ever more sophisticated computer-based process and management control systems are adopted. In their place comes a much greater emphasis upon the process development and innovation side of the production manager's job. This trend seems likely in the manufacturing environment and it may well require a radically different set of skills to undertake this role from the typical set of competencies exhibited in most industries today.

The way in which certain technologies can have a major impact upon employment patterns is well illustrated by the necessary interrelatedness of firms which supply to those companies pursuing inventory reduction and 'just in time' initiatives. The goal of JIT demands a close relationship between the supplier and the supplied. This relationship has to give an absolute guarantee of both quality and delivery and, as many companies have found, requires a detailed integration of supplier systems with client company.

We can therefore see that organisational boundaries are becoming considerably blurred. A packaging company supplying to a major electronics company illustrates this well. The purpose of subcontracting the packaging and shipping of computer components was to reduce costs through inventory reduction and overheads. Furthermore, the work is not seen by the client company to be core to their business Through the introduction of JIT and all the consequent quality and delivery certification the systems of the two companies became closely integrated. There is a small resident team of people from the client company in the supplier's premises ensuring effective operation of the contract. One of the reasons why the subcontractor is able to provide such a cost-effective service is that his labour costs are considerably lower than those of the client company. Conditions, guarantees of employment, welfare and benefits are all better in the client company. The very integration of the systems now forces two highly incompatible (in employee relations terms) organisations together, causing tension and a pressure to harmonise employment relationships between the two. The paradox is that to concede to this pressure will jeopardise the entire arrangement, as the costs of the service will then become prohibitive.

Whether, therefore, supplier relationships which are as integrated as that described in the above example can be justified in the long term solely on cost grounds is debatable. The supplier should have advantage based on specialist understanding and operations, but in the long term not based on major differences in labour rates and conditions.

The second question the example raises is the boundaries we place upon operations management where a company is wholly reliant on a wide range of single-source suppliers. Should the manager see part of the management of the operation as being in fact a detailed management, or at least co-ordination, of his or her suppliers? Many will say 'no', until a stoppage or disruption at a supplier's premises brings the whole process to a shuddering halt. Then there comes the pressure to intervene when it is too late. IBM, Marks and Spencer, Ford and the Rover Group are examples of companies increasingly becoming involved in the internal affairs of their suppliers.

Summary

To achieve high rates of change and innovation organisations need to be prepared to be much more flexible in the employment options they offer. The predominant view that there should be harmonised terms and conditions for all members of staff will in some respects have to break down. It is unlikely that R&D staff, for example, will respond to the uniformity which will be prevalent in the operational areas.

This greater diversity of employment patterns will introduce new organisational tensions which will have to be appropriately managed. The price of eliminating these tensions may well be the stifling of innovation and change.

Recruitment and selection

A word is required about how we can actively recruit and select those who will have the greatest chance of innovating, as well as those who will need to be responsive to the innovative culture.

We are constantly reminded of the inefficiency, if not the downright ineffectiveness, of face-to-face interviewing as a means of selection. A recent study[8] suggests that interviewing used on its own as a selection technique has a 3 per cent better success rate in getting you the right person than pure chance. Even the most reliable selection methods score only 21 per cent above chance, and this was using the 'in-tray technique' whereby candidates are given a series of exercises as close to real life as possible to perform, involving letters, data, problems, and so on. If we couple this with the undoubted difficulty of spotting the extent to which the organisation itself inhibits innovation then we have in selection a complex task which some would say is impossible.

A Swedish consulting group has recently built upon Pinchot's book (see Chapter 2) and developed a programme for intrapreneurs. This takes the form of a series of selection workshops where embryonic intrapreneurs are alleged to be spotted, who are then built and developed through work-shops and training. Some doubts have been expressed about whether innovators or intrapreneurs, if we insist on the jargon, can so easily be systematised. In Tom Peters' comments about the idea of the UK's Management Charter he states that he despises the word 'professional'. He believes we need instead managers who love innovation, quality and people. Peters shies away from prescriptions asking for flexibility, opportunism, vision and entrepreneurship.

The current ideas on management competence, which have been built upon the ideas of Boyatsis,[9] are primarily looking at what we describe as the maintenance management activities. They are necessarily important to deliver the products and services of past change and innovation, which we must never lose sight of. It is too easy to suggest that we should now recruit and train for innovation and forget that we must still deliver consistently to the marketplace.

None of this is helpful if we are to encourage and develop innovation. If we are doubtful about selection and pessimistic about training, then how can we hope to achieve success? There are a number of guidelines.

Innovation is an uncertain and risky process with high potential rewards. We need to place emphasis on the innovative environment where a wide range of people can have the opportunity to be innovative. In this way individuals will largely self-select through achievement.

In a recent study of management practices among high-technology companies in Scotland[10] it is apparent that there are an increasing number of employers using a wide range of analytical testing techniques for selection, even for junior and low-skill jobs. Of particular interest is the extent to which these tests concentrate on attitude and aptitude rather than specific skills and experience: attitudes towards cooperation, change, work and flexibility, and aptitudes for learning and accepting change. It is in this way that such companies ensure as far as possible that their employees fit the culture and environment as a priority. It is becoming increasingly important to have 'change' skills; the investment is needed both for immediate needs and for ensuring that in the future we have people who are adaptable and susceptible to training and development.

A useful set of selection criteria and selection ideas has been developed by Majaro.[11] He identifies creative managers as having:

- Conceptual fluency: the ability to generate ideas.
- Mental fluency: the ability to shift from one way of thinking to another.
- Originality: being able to give unusual answers to conventional questions, looking at issues in very different ways.
- The ability to suspend judgement. Many of us fall into the trap of

making instant judgements on new ideas. Many of these judgements are negative. The innovator will suspend judgement on new and different ideas until they have been thoroughly worked through.

- Impulse acceptance. Creative people are often impulsive, as ideas capture their imagination.
- A challenging attitude to authority. Those with ideas are going to be less accepting of authority than those who have none. This is particularly difficult to accept for many companies. The job adverts will almost always ask for innovatory, creative and dynamic candidates; what they do not say is that you must not rock the boat. Creative people must challenge the existing order, and that is a difficult pill to swallow.
- Tolerance. A creative person will be tolerant of others' ideas; it is most often with others that ideas are built upon and innovation occurs.

There are a range of tests and tools which can indicate these attributes. Of course these attributes have to be seen in addition to the required technical knowledge and experience. Quite often the full set of attributes will not rest to a great extent in one person, and that is where help can be given to the composition of the team. Belbin's[11] a managerial team types can give useful insights into the components of an innovative team. Belbin suggests that effective teams require a range of complementary skills. The team managing technological change thus requires a range of skills, which can be provided only by the right mix of people.

It is only once innovation and change have become part of a company that the most likely entrepreneurs can surface. There is a range of initiatives which can promote this:

- top management being clearly interested in ideas for improvement at all levels of the organisation;
- ensuring that managers see their job security in terms of innovation and change rather than maintaining the present;
- making creativity and innovation a key performance measure through appraisal and performance management systems;
- rewarding, promoting and developing those people who have delivered change rather than leaving them to wallow in specialist functions.

Summary

There is no foolproof way of selecting individuals who are going to champion technological change. There are, however, indicators, and these should be used to assist rather than to determine recruitment decisions. It is highly unlikely that any individual is going to be successful in an unsupportive organisational environment. Every organisation requires a 'critical mass' of people who thrive on innovation and change. In such an environment those who appear to have the attributes of innovators will have the best opportunity to succeed.

Pay structure and pay design

The way we pay ourselves and others gives some very strong messages about what we deem to be important in the organisation. Too often we find that the pay system objectives are not in concordance with the business objectives. Much is written on the myriad of different ways in which we can pay our staff. Much less is written on the impact this actually has on the organisation's behaviour. The trend in the western world is towards the individualisation of pay based upon individual contribution. This is fine in principle if individual effort is what we wish to reward and if it can be measured. The danger comes when we find that measurement is difficult and that it is complex teamwork which will lead to success, and probably over a long period of time. The introduction of a short-term series of measures based on individual activity will actively discourage innovation. If pay is a short-term measure then our approach to innovation inevitably will be corroded into 'short termism'. The pay system therefore places a strong stamp on the culture of the company.

It is not realistic to put our boards of directors on highly geared, performance-linked remuneration packages based on the extent to which profit targets are exceeded and then to talk about innovation and creativity. It is just not credible. We presumably introduced the scheme to encourage short-term profit increase and to modify the behaviour of our senior management accordingly. What choice would you make when the options are half a million pounds of investment for an interesting but unproven idea or 10 per cent of this in the directors' bonus pot? If we believe our directors not to be influenced in such a crude manner, then why do we introduce such a crude incentive scheme?

A similar logic applies throughout the organisation. A large company, after much planning and deliberation, decided to change their output-based incentive scheme. It was a long haul, but in the end agreement was reached to replace it with a reward structure which was based on total factory performance improvement. Now for the first time there is real interest in joint problem solving and genuinely making suggestions for improvement. The pay system will not of itself change much, but it will radically change the environment in which we work. Pay systems are rarely neutral in their effect on the innovation culture of an organisation. Some can promote creativity; many can retard it.

It is quite clear from many studies that of more importance to technologists than money is the opportunity to develop their ideas with the necessary support and help. Of course, if they can become rich at the same time then we have a winning combination!

Employee involvement

Employee involvement is a loosely defined concept which conjures up in most managers' minds a woolly series of notions inflicted upon the organisation by the personnel function. The change that is slowly coming into the boardrooms of our companies is that employee involvement is becoming a business imperative for competitive advantage. Everything from the total quality concept to innovation requires far higher degrees of employee commitment and involvement than we have ever encouraged before, and most innovative companies can confirm their value.

In what we have previously called the bureaucratic or segmented organisation there is very little scope for change and innovation. The new starter is soon told that this is the way we do things around here, the strong message being, 'put up or shut up, and do not rock the boat'. The immediate boss has little freedom to act and would need higher approval to make minor changes. He or she too will be discouraged from making changes.

In the survival days of the late 1970s and early 1980s a breed of chief executives who had their fingers on everyone's pulse was highly rated; they worked harder, knew more, interfered with everything, were able to recite warehouse breakages and retail managers' failures. The energy and enthusiasm were great, but the net effect was to freeze everyone else into inaction; the boss always knew better. To create and innovate needs a looser rein: no less energy and no less enthusiasm, but redirected to enabling others to envision the future and deliver it.

In the segmented, top-driven company there are few aspects of the business which are open to challenge except by the most senior of the executives. There are no Brownie points for stepping out of line. Executives have for too long been primarily focused on internal concerns such as performance and productivity. These concerns, whilst legitimate, cannot be their sole preoccupation if the organisation is to continue to be successful. What is additionally required is an external market focus which can capture change and opportunity. If we look at the impact of this transition on employee involvement we can start to see the shift from inwardly focused activities such as problem solving and quality groups to creativity teams which look outside our current boundaries of problem definition into opportunities for the future. Majoro[13] in his book *The Creative Gap*, sees this transition as one from quality circles to creativity circles. The idea is captured in a different way by Tom Peters in his *Thriving on Chaos*,[14] when he draws a boat representing the organisation and a water line representing the extent to which organisations are open to creativity and change. For the organisation with a high water line there are few aspects of the business which are open to challenge except by the most senior of the executives. This is the organisation where people are told to stick to their jobs and not to interfere in other people's work and activity. On the other hand, there is the business with a low water line. This is the organisation where challenge and debate are valued, the only unchallengeable feature being the purpose of the business itself.

This openness and challenge is particularly threatening to management who rely upon their position of power and control to influence their organisations. This is where employee involvement becomes both real and difficult to handle. Most often it is spoken of and acted upon as though it is something for the lower ranks and, if successful, can help to reinforce more senior managers' ideas and programmes. The key question is whether we are prepared to have our ideas and actions challenged, questioned and changed. Employee involvement which is truly creative will pose a threat to those who currently wield the power, and will demand a major act of courage from them and from the newly empowered.

This challenge most often comes when employee involvement is invited through one of many mechanisms such as quality circles, problem-solving groups and suggestion schemes. How such activities are handled is crucial to creating the open participative environment which promotes innovation.

Suggestion schemes

As with the broader area of employee involvement, companies are now re-examining their attitude to one of the lowest priorities on the managerial map: the suggestion scheme. Most companies have such a scheme, usually a battered box labelled 'suggestions' (that is, if the paint has not entirely peeled off and the box has not fallen off the wall). The process has too often become isolated and neglected. A tatty form is filled in by someone who is often seen by their colleagues as a smart aleck trying to ingratiate themselves with the management. Once a month the personnel officer picks up the forms and files them away until the suggestions committee meets – a poorly attended, infrequent affair at which evaluation is carried out – and a few derisory awards are given several months later. The final insult to the idea is the picture in the company newspaper a year after the suggestion, showing the cheque being handed over. The overall impression: 'We are not really interested in your ideas, but at least it is a good cop-out for the supervisors when confronted with an idea on the night shift; they merely reply, "I'd fill out a suggestion form if I were you".'

Suggestion schemes can be very effective. They can give a strong cultural lead, they can be practical, and they can generate incremental and step changes. There are a number of guidelines:

- Give the process a high profile.
- Give quick feedback, i.e. within days of submission.
- Take ideas seriously.
- Follow them up with the individual and his or her team.
- Involve the work team's boss.
- Allow others to build on good ideas.
- Praise the initiative, whatever the worth of the idea.
- Demonstrate quick action on good ideas.
- Allocate managerial resources to the programme or drop it.

Quality circles

We have looked at the need for multifunctional teams managing change. Quality circles are a specific subset of these ideas, the success of which is entirely dependent upon the extent to which we really do wish to improve quality and can accept the consequences of so doing.[15] Plenty has been written on the subject; it is not the intention here to reiterate all the current practice.

The important issues are the scope of such teams' activity, the support they receive and their scope for implementation. Innovative companies have evolved the concept of quality circles dealing with immediate problems towards creativity teams. Quality circles have largely been interpreted as a shop-floor phenomenon and that is often where they have stuck. If the idea is to become effective that way of working must be demonstrated and practised from the top down.

People systems

A particular concern is the extent to which people systems choke and stifle innovation within organisations. Reference has already been made to a number of these, e.g. the pay system, how the organisation communicates and how it recruits; there are others.

The inheritance of the personnel profession seems to be largely a set of systems and procedures which serve to apply consistency, order and conformity to an organisation. Job evaluation, for example, has required managers and others to describe their tasks (not their achievement or contribution) over the past years with a view to subjecting this description to a pseudo-scientific process. Many millions of pounds have been poured into this pursuit; and to what end? An assumption that the past will continue into the future? That tasks rather than achievements make businesses successful? That maintenance has far more value than development?

Table 4.4 New v. old human resource philosophies

	Old	New
Underlying philosophy	People are a cost which needs to be minimised	The company can never get enough good people
		People, no matter what grade or skill level, are ultimately the greatest source of competitive advantage and need continuous development
Recruiting	'Milkround' approach, hired by personnel managers	Screen by campus manager, or by a personnel manager (who is probably a line manager on rotation in personnel)
		Interviews with up to six people who will work with an individual candidate
(Re)training	Hire/fire to get the right skills	Retrain, instead of firing and hiring
	Many largely organised, scheduled and run by personnel departments	Minimal intervention by a personnel function (infrastructure setting only)
		Most training needs determined by managers using multiple internal and external suppliers
Development	Single-track functional career path	Rotation through functions
	'Dead men's shoes'	Rotation through geographies
		Internal career development and progress to reinforce corporate culture
		Fast-track programmes
Appraisal, incentives and rewards	Technical skills rewarded with promotion	Appraised explicitly on many different skill categories: technical, leadership, teamwork
	Salary structure often determined by unions and common to many employers	Individuals' objectives set in accordance with corporate strategy
		Aggressive competition on salaries
		Linkages between income and personal and corporate performance

Source: NEDC (1988) *Performance and Competitive Success in the UK Electronics Industry*.

Job evaluation places in concrete a rigid structure of relationships. The development jobs of an innovative organisation are amoebic, difficult to define and constantly changing. Micrometers are not very helpful in evaluating such jobs. Of course, some form of relative structure is required, but this can be very simple and place much more emphasis on delivery and contribution.

Performance measurement and appraisal can give contrary messages. If our measures of performance are achievement of budget and keeping manpower at the predetermined level, then these are the key priorities we present to our managers. Exhortations about change and technology will fall on deaf ears if this is how we judge people.

Some guidelines for the development of the people systems are:

- Set objectives and appraise and reward people for innovating for the future.
- Set long-term as well as short-term goals.
- Simplify job and grading structures.
- Don't let artificial organisational barriers get in your way.
- Align people with the organisation's values and priorities.
- Help people to distinguish between short-term and long-term actions.
- Support both the values and the behaviours which will deliver what is needed.

Table 4.4 summarises some of the major changes in people or human resource systems identified for the UK's electronics sector.

The trade union response to the introduction of advanced technology

The early 1960s saw the first post-war trade union interest in the impact of what was then seen as automation on working people and their trade unions. Predictions were made at this time that jobs would be savagely cut as a result of further mechanisation, particularly in the manufacturing sector. No such crisis came; the crises that did were interpreted in a different way, most often economic. The late 1970s and early 1980s saw a further acceleration in the trade union concern as 'electronics' appeared to be a major cause of job reduction. Because of this, coupled with economic stagnation, there was a pressure to maintain jobs, and emphasis was placed upon 'new technology agreements'. These were designed to be a means by which the introduction of technological change would be negotiated or jointly decided upon between trade unions and management. The reality was often very different. The processes of technological change became too varied to be susceptible to rigid procedures, and the economic climate dictated a 'take it or leave it' attitude on the part of many organisations. At best these agreements provided a communications and consultative structure which assisted the overall task of gaining commitment to and understanding of the desired changes.

The overall ineffectiveness of new technology agreements should not be taken to imply that the issues they sought to address were irrelevant or unimportant to the processes of technological change. The problem rather is that such agreements have not proven to be an effective instrument for either trade unions or management in resolving issues to do with job reduction, job security, removal of demarcation, pay, retraining and flexibility.

It is unrealistic to expect staff, whether unionised or not, deliberately to do themselves out of a job. Furthermore, without some job security it is difficult to see how people are going to be prepared to stick their necks out and make incremental or radical suggestions for improvement.

Trade union power fluctuates with time in any economic system. The current low level of power of trade unions in the western economies must not be interpreted as a sign that the issues which they champion have died away. Riding roughshod over the legitimate interests of employees in the introduction of advanced technology will in the long run be to the detriment of the organisation's performance. For unionised companies this may come back to haunt them when trade union power next increases.

Summary

The organisational implications of successful technological change are wide and varied. Concentration on the technical aspects is insufficient; the technology has to be managed alongside the management and development of the organisation. The questions for managers are:

- Who is responsible for managing the organisational implications of technological change in your organisation?
- How aware are your technologists of these implications?
- Does your corporate strategy recognise the impact it has on technological innovation and investment?

References

1. Voss, C. A. (1986) In Twiss, B. (ed.) *Implementing Manufacturing Technology in the 1990s*, MCB.

2. Goold, M and Campbell, A (1987) *Strategies and Styles*. Blackwell.
3. National Economic Development Council (1988) *Performance and Competitive Success in the UK Electronics Industry*.
4. Sorge, Arndt et al (1983) *Microelectronics and Manpower in Manufacturing*, Gower.
5. Burnes, B. and Fitter, M. (1987) Control of advanced manufacturing technology: supervision without supervisors? In Wall, T. (ed.) *The Human Side of Advanced Manufacturing Technology*, Wiley.
6. UK Biotech 88 (1988) *Industry in Evolution?* Arthur Young/AABB.
7. Wild, R. (1987) Changing manufacturing technologies and policies, and the role of manufacturing managers. In Twiss, B. (ed.) *Operations Management in the 1990s*. MCB.
8. Robertson and Smith, UMIST unpublished.
9. Boyatsis, R. E. (1982) *The Competent Manager*. Wiley.
10. Goodridge, M. and Cameron, J. (1988) *Management Training for New Employee Relations Practices*. Training Agency.
11. Majaro, S. (1988) *The Creative Gap*. Longman.
12. Belbin, M. (1981) *Management Teams* Heinemann.
13. Ibid.
14. Peters, T. J. (1988) *Thriving on Chaos*. Macmillan.
15. Bartlett, J. B. (1983) *Success and Failure in Quality Circles*, Employment Relations.

5 Identification and management of innovative opportunities

In the preceding chapters we have discussed the environmental, strategic and organisational factors that provide the background within which a technical change takes place. They do not ensure that successful change projects will be forthcoming. This depends upon the identification, design and implementation of specific proposals consistent with the requirements identified earlier.

Technical change is the application of knowledge new to the company in order to create corporate wealth or solve a problem. It takes the form of a new product or service where the application is outside the company, or a new operational or managerial system when it is inside. Thus the process of technical change can be seen to involve the linking of technology to an internal or external need. Furthermore, it must do this in a way which yields a greater profit to the company than would have been the case without it. However, it must be recognised that the costs of development and introduction are likely to involve some sacrifice of short-term profit in order to achieve the company's long-term aims.

The three main headings under which this process will be examined are illustrated in Fig. 5.1. The technical change process converts intellectual and physical inputs into a form which satisfies the needs of a user. It is useful also to draw a distinction between the physical and the non-physical flows. If one takes the motorcar as an example, the physical flow consists of materials and equipment which are then operated upon in a series of manufacturing operations to produce the finished product which the customer buys. The non-physical flow is the application of technical knowledge, for example combustion theory or metallurgy, to satisfy the attributes needed by the user, some of which are psychological, for

Fig. 5.1 Inputs and outputs of the technical change process

example status and security. Both these flows are interlinked at all stages. It is this second flow that is of increasing importance in two respects. First, the technical content is providing the major contribution to enhanced performance, signifying a greater intellectual input: brains rather than brawn. Secondly, as we have seen earlier, the psychological satisfactions are becoming more important to many customers whose basic material needs are met by existing products. Because of the traditional focus on the physical processes it might appear that the emphasis we place on the intellectual flows is conceptual and academic. This is not so.

There is one additional element which has not been included in Fig. 5.1. That is creativity. It might be argued that a rational analysis of user needs combined with a systematic assessment of the potential provided by technology would lead logically to the identification of the ideas upon which a technical change should be based. Such an analysis is highly desirable, and can lead to adequate solutions, but it is unlikely to reveal really innovative solutions. That depends upon the exercise of human imagination and creativity.

The identification of needs

Ideas for technical change can originate anywhere. This is a truism often overlooked. Thus it must be a concern of everyone in the company. The innovation literature often concentrates upon the rival merits of technology push and market pull. The dominance of one of these modes is likely to reflect the culture of the company and the relative strengths of technology and marketing. Where R&D is strong and communication with the market poor, technical considerations may dominate the change process, frequently with disastrous results if the needs of the users are insufficiently appreciated. Conversely, where marketing is strong the technical departments can become subservient to an extent which eliminates their potential for originating innovative products. A meeting of minds between these two departments is only one, albeit often the most important, of the many linkages which can lead to ideas for change. We shall now examine some of the most valuable of these sources of ideas.

Research and development

Technical knowledge enables R&D to appreciate the potential of technological advances. These they will wish to exploit and the initiative will come from them: technology push. Their ideas are often associated with radical departures from current practice. Research indicates, however, that technology push is responsible for a relatively small proportion of new products. However, those that are successful often incorporate the most radical ideas, which subsequently lead to families of market-led improvements. Thus their small number understates their economic importance.

No technology-push change will succeed unless it satisfies a need. Unfortunately, it is often difficult to assess in advance whether the perceived need is a market reality. Conventional market research and the marketing department may be of little assistance with something where there is no past experience. A careful assessment of the attributes of the technology linked to market attributes in conjunction with the estimated costs of development and of the product is the only method of assisting management judgement. The risks are high, but so are the rewards for success. But for every success – TV, video recorders, plastics – there are failures – the video telephone, quadraphonics, Corfam. The incidence of purely technical failures is relatively low, although the costs of development may be much higher than expected. The failures mostly occur in the marketplace, for reasons which are usually clear after the event (e.g. the lack of an attribute the customer really wanted or too high a product cost) but which are difficult to assess accurately in advance.

Similar considerations apply to less radical technically originated ideas and also in the application of new technology in areas other than products. This source of ideas must be encouraged, since it is the main avenue for introducing new technology into the company. It must be appreciated that from time to time they will lead to significant contributions to the company. However, it must also be recognised that the establishment of technical feasibility is only the first, though essential, step towards successful technical change.

Marketing

Due to its proximity to the customer the marketing department is most sensitive to user needs and is likely to generate the largest number of ideas for new products. In these, incremental improvements rather than entirely new products or services are likely to predominate. Where the company is marketing led this usually presents no problem. However, in many companies there is a reluctance of R&D to accept market-initiated ideas on the grounds of technical infeasibility and without careful consideration.

The main direct interface between the company and its customers is its sales force. It is they who hear the users' complaints or their ideas for new products. This knowledge often remains at this level and is not transmitted back into the company through marketing to the technical department, except when there is a serious design fault. The reasons for this are likely to be organisational. If the role of the sales force is seen to be confined to selling and their payment system is related to their sales volume, then they have no incentive to devote their energies to collecting and communicating information for which they receive no reward. This factor can also be an influence on the rate of growth of a new product. In general it will require more effort to initiate sales than for the more established products, hence the payment system can provide a disincentive for the sales force to promote it.

Effective communication between the technical and the marketing departments is essential. This is so obvious that there seems little point in stressing it. Yet research and the experience of the authors indicate that this is still a major cause of failure. It can be overcome only when they have a common objective deriving from the company's organisational and managerial systems.

Other departments

In many instances the user of a technical change is within the company itself, e.g. a manufacturing process by the production department or an information system by the finance department. Similar considerations to those above apply, although to some extent the role of the marketing department in respect of new products must now be assumed by the technical department.

Users

Users, be they the purchasers of a product or those affected by a technical change within the company, are the people most aware of its merits or shortcomings. However, the superior technical knowledge of the supplier often engenders in the supplier company an attitude that it knows best what is good for the user. In some cases the buyer is sophisticated and can provide invaluable information to the supplier. In other cases buyers may be less educated and unable to articulate their needs clearly. Attention to the user can make a valuable contribution in three ways: development of existing products or processes, knowledge of how they are used in practice, and ideas for innovations.

Development of existing products

Research by von Hippel[1] at MIT has shown that users often modify manufacturers' equipment to better suit their needs; for example, he found that in the semiconductor and electronic subassembly process equipment industry the relative proportions of innovative products first developed by users were 67 per cent compared with 33 per cent by the manufacturers (sample size 49), and in scientific instruments the proportions were 77 per cent compared with 23 per cent (sample size 111). Sometimes this may take the form of a minor modification to meet operational requirements. In other cases it may result from a costly development programme. There is a financial logic to this. The cost of the modification to the user may be justified because of its benefits in terms of, say, reduced manufacturing costs using the equipment, whereas the return on investment to the supplier through increased equipment price may not be adequate to justify the development. In other words, the RoI to the user is greater than to the supplier. But once this development cost has been incurred the modification may be available to the supplier at little or no cost. The lesson is clear. Observe closely the way your products are used or modified and incorporate these changes yourself in order to provide a superior product.

Knowledge of how the product is used in practice

In most products the users cannot modify. They must accept what they are offered or purchase from another supplier. For a technical change applied within the company, deficiencies may lead to operational problems. The technical change is not 'user friendly', be it software or a physical product. This occurs because the designers do not use the systems themselves or are unable or unwilling to identify with the needs of the users.

There is no effective substitute for hands-on experience by the designers, although this may not always be possible. In some companies R&D staff are even forbidden to have direct contact with the customer, this being regarded as the prerogative of marketing. The larger the company, the more likely it is that the technologist becomes isolated from the user. This managerial isolation is not confined to lack of contact with the users of products. Many technologists and managers spend insufficient time on the shop floor. Peters and Waterman[2] refer to the need to 'manage by walking about'. It must be recognised that ideas for change often occur in a random fashion and can surface from casual chance encounters. It is a case of not knowing what you are looking for until you have found it. Management must actively encourage designers to gain operational experience of the products they design or observe how they are used.

Ideas for new products

Although the users may be unaware of what is technically feasible, they do have a good appreciation of what products or services they would like to have if the price were right. This can be a valuable source of ideas when there is a willingness to listen and a system for transferring the ideas into the company. Many consumer-product companies establish consumer panels for this purpose. Occasionally motor manufacturers will design 'concept cars' to test the reactions of potential customers. The aim should be to involve the user in the design at as early a stage as is feasible and to maintain a continuing dialogue.

An alternative is to invite user reactions to a new product before it is launched, perhaps through a test market or discussions with opinion leaders. Although this is desirable it is a poor substitute for involving them in the early development or concept generation stages. All too often, particularly in the engineering industry, the customers are faced with a *fait accompli*: 'take it or leave it'. The high failure rate of new products is a clear indication that many customers adopt the latter alternative.

Top management

Their wide range of outside contacts and their knowledge of the total corporate scene enable top management to gain insights of what changes are desirable. This is particularly true where functional demarcations are rigid and a corporate approach exists only at the most senior level. In general they do not possess the detailed knowledge to suggest how their ideas can be achieved in practice. In some cases their ideas may not be technically feasible. Because of this their suggestions are often ridiculed and rejected at lower levels. Sometimes they will be forced through to success in spite of this opposition.

Competitors

No company can be expected to have all the good ideas. Many ideas are developed by competitors and, when not covered by patents, are available for all to use. This may apply to new products or to improvements to existing products. Some companies purchase all the competitive products and examine them meticulously, but many neglect this valuable source of ideas. To some it may appear to reflect upon their own innovative skills. In others it is a manifestation of the 'not invented here' syndrome. It is not an admission of failure, nor is it a surrender of technical leadership, if one's own, possibly innovative, products incorporate ideas proven by others. However, because of this common reluctance, it is important that management ensure that there is a formal system for monitoring and assessing competitive products and learning from what they find.

Other employees

All employees are users in the sense that it is they who have the hands-on experience of manufacturing the products, offering the service, using the management systems and dealing with customers. They are a fruitful source of ideas for change to overcome any shortcomings which many managements do not fully exploit. In most cases their proposals are likely to be relatively minor but, because of their number, they can in aggregate be of significant value.

We have already noted that a high volume of bottom–up communication is a feature of the innovative firm. Quality circles and suggestion boxes are two means by which this participation can be achieved, but they often fail because of an unwillingness by management to accept the change proposals. This is illustrated by a comparison between the USA and Japan which shows some important differences (Table 5.1).

Table 5.1 Comparison of US and Japanese workers' involvement

	USA	Japan
Rate of worker participation	14%	58.3%
Number of suggestions per worker	0.15	14.74
Percentage adopted by management	24%	75.9%

Source: Japan Human Relations Association (1983)
US Association of Suggestion Schemes (1978)

These figures indicate not only the high involvement of Japanese workers but more importantly the high rate of acceptance of their ideas by management. Although there has been increasing attention paid to these schemes in Western countries in recent years, there is no reason to believe that the current situation is significantly different from that indicated by these figures.

In many cases employees introduce innovations without management becoming aware of them, thus limiting their total potential. In one investigation in a number of US companies it was found that up to 60 per cent of computer hardware and 40 per cent of software innovations were introduced without the involvement of the data-processing department. Whilst the individual changes may be relatively slight, they can in aggregate become significant.

In order to improve the identification of user needs management should address the following questions:

- Where have the ideas originated for new products, processes and systems developed in the past?

- Are we fully exploiting the potential of all sources of possible user needs that can be satisfied by the application of technology?
- How can we improve the flow of ideas from underutilised sources?
- Are there any organisational barriers to the communication of user needs and, if so, how can they be removed?

Technology capture and transfer

The technology a company uses is, for the most part, created outside it. Even the most R&D-intensive firms are only minor actors on the world stage. For example, the UK accounts for only about 5 per cent of total world R&D expenditure. Thus most of the knowledge of commercial value is generated in other companies, universities and research institutes throughout the world: much of it may be published in foreign languages. Gaining access to this knowledge and making use of what is valuable are matters that cannot be left to chance. The process of technology capture and transfer can be considered as occurring in three stages – identification of sources of knowledge, the use of these sources, and the transfer of the knowledge into the company – although there will inevitably be some degree of overlap.

Identification of sources

This is the process whereby those individuals or organisations who are most likely to provide exploitable knowledge are identified. They may be of value in their own right or because of their position in one or more informal networks. Such networks are becoming of increasing importance as the volume of knowledge and the variety of sources of it have expanded. Thus it has become difficult, if not impossible, for any organisation to identify and monitor them all without assistance. The networks (Fig. 5.2) help in this process by providing access to members of other networks who can act as preliminary information gatherers and filters.

Use of sources

The type of knowledge required for technical change falls into two classes. The first category is information which is required to satisfy a known need in a field where there is an existing expertise. Routine scanning of the many data bases available nowadays and monitoring of known developments can be of great assistance, although the time lags between a technological advance and its publication may be a considerable problem when

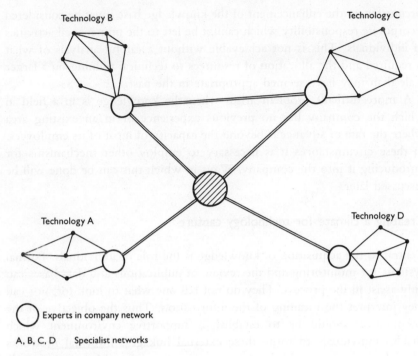

Technology B

Technology C

Technology A

Technology D

○ Experts in company network

A, B, C, D   Specialist networks

Fig. 5.2 Information networks

progress is rapid. In such cases it is essential to gain access before publication through an informal network. The second category is the acquisition of knowledge which is new in the sense that there is no way that its existence could be known about in advance. This is another example of not knowing what you are looking for until you have found it. This can be the most valuable source for generating ideas for technical change and is likely to be acquired in a random fashion from contacts with the sources already identified and from membership of the networks.

Transfer of the knowledge

New knowledge is of no use until it is applied within the company. Where it lies within fields where there is an existing competence this should present little difficulty, since it can be absorbed easily into the firm's knowledge base. However, it should not be assumed that this will occur naturally without encouragement and training. At one time it was possible for technologists to equip themselves for life at the time of their initial training. They would need to keep abreast of new developments, but this was not a major problem when the range of technologies relevant to their needs was unchanging and the rate of progress relatively slow. In today's circumstances the enhancement of the knowledge base must be considered a corporate responsibility which cannot be left to the unmanaged activities of individuals. This is not achievable without a careful analysis of what is required and the allocation of resources to technical training on a larger scale than may have seemed appropriate in the past.

A more difficult problem arises when the knowledge is in a field in which the company has no previous experience or in an existing area where the rate of advance is beyond the capacity of most of its employees. In these circumstances it is necessary to employ other mechanisms for introducing it into the company. Ways in which this can be done will be discussed later.

Creating a climate for technology capture

Central to the acquisition of knowledge is the role of individuals. Formal systems for monitoring and the review of publications and data bases can only assist in the process. They do not tell one what to look for; nor can they interpret the meaning of the information. Thus the objective of the organisation should be to establish a supportive environment which enables individuals to forge these external linkages. Informal networks depend upon the establishment of personal relationships with people outside the company. Research has shown that the most successful companies:

- support external and international contacts;
- support professional visits;
- encourage conference attendance;
- encourage continuous education.

All these activities cost money. In many companies they are viewed with suspicion, since it is usually impossible to justify in advance a proposal, for example attending an overseas conference, in terms of specific benefits. The costs can be quantified, but the benefits are often intangible and long-term. Furthermore, they can involve the absence of senior technologists from their place of work for considerable periods. But it must be recognised that these activities are as essential to the corporate wellbeing as close contacts with customers.

Examination of the information flow processes within an organisation reveals another characteristic. There are some individuals who, because of their natural curiosity and interest, read widely and have an extensive range of personal informal professional contacts. As a consequence they acquire a great deal of random information, much of which may have little immediate relevance or relationship to their formal duties. However, when a problem arises they are often consulted by their colleagues. On some occasions they may be able to provide an answer, but more frequently they can suggest an external contact who is able to assist. These people are called 'gatekeepers'. All organisations possess them.

It must be appreciated that gatekeepers cannot be appointed, but organisations should recognise the important role they can perform in the knowledge acquisition process. They should be identified, used and encouraged to take an active part in the dissemination of information throughout the company. Perhaps more importantly, they should not be discouraged; this can easily happen, since much of the gatekeeping activity is performed during the firm's time at the expense of their formal duties.

In recent years attention has focused on the 'gatekeeper role'[3] rather than the part played by a few individual gatekeepers, which is seen as 'overcoming the constraints of organisational form'. Attention should be directed to the need to involve as many people as possible in the task of gaining access to external information and transferring it into the company, although inevitably some people will be more active than others. Research has shown that firms that stress participation and *bottomup* communication provide an organisational structure which fosters this process.

Although most attention has been paid to the technological gatekeeper there is evidence to suggest that this role is also important in other business functions, e.g. marketing, finance, personnel and legal.

Managing technology transfer

Some aspects of technology transfer have already been discussed. Attention is now turned to ways for incorporating a new technology or new knowledge where the company does not possess an in-house capability of using it. The difficulty of developing a competence in a new area must not be underestimated.

The most satisfactory method, where appropriate, is to recruit a person who is an expert in the field. This obvious solution is often frustrated by an unwillingness to offer such a person a salary commensurate with his or her worth. This is a particular problem in the large company with formal and rigid salary scales, where it is difficult to offer a sufficient inducement without introducing an anomaly into the payment system, something which the personnel department is likely to resist. Many innovative companies adopt a much more flexible attitude to payment. Although the desire for standardisation is understandable, it may be a shortsighted policy if it results in the loss of an individual who can make a critical contribution. The need for greater flexibility is stressed by Sir

John Harvey-Jones, former Chairman of ICI, in the following quotation from his recent book.[4]

Companies will have to be more flexible in their demands, to accommodate more and more the individual's different hopes, wishes and ambitions, To do this is not easy, for it means in turn abandoning many of the systems of personnel management, and taking far more responsibility for encouraging and supporting difference. In all large companies there is a lot of comfort derived from administrative systems that purport to be 'fair' but in reality remove from individual managers the responsibility of trying to reward and administer people's careers while allowing for differences which are immeasurable in quantitative terms.

Where the need for an injection of new knowledge is temporary, for example the installation of a computer-based system or research to solve a short-term problem, it is often more appropriate to use an outside agency, e.g. a consultancy or a contract research organisation. This does not, however, fully satisfy the transfer needs, since it must be recognised that the ownership of the problem remains with the company and the outside agency is unlikely to have either a full understanding of the company's operational circumstances or a long-term commitment. Problems are likely to be encountered unless one individual is appointed to be responsible for all aspects of the implementation. This cannot be delegated to outsiders or diffused within the organisation. There may also be a significant training need for those who will be involved with the operation or incorporation of the new technology. These needs must be identified at an early stage in order to ensure a smooth hand-over. A common feature of technical changes that experience implementation difficulties is the neglect of training until a late stage in the process. It should be an integral part of the planning from the beginning.

Licensing is another alternative. This is an important means of acquiring new knowledge without the costs of development, which have been incurred elsewhere. It is beyond the scope of this book to discuss the many aspects of licensing agreements, which must be managed carefully. Nevertheless, there is much evidence to suggest that companies underrate the value of licensing and engage in expensive developments to duplicate what can be purchased more cheaply from outside.

The acquisition of knowledge in a new technology which is of critical importance for the future of the firm may sometimes require more radical and strategic actions. Some of these have already been discussed in Chapter 1 and include:

- take-over of or merger with a company that can provide the technical expertise that is lacking;
- collaboration with other companies, including competitors, by means of:

(a) joint ventures;
(b) jointly funded pre-competitive research;
(c) shared development costs;
(d) technical exchange agreements.

In high-technology industries much of the new knowledge is generated in universities. The transfer of this knowledge into a commercial organisation presents many problems. Although university faculties have become accustomed to working more closely with industry, often through contract research, this does not remove the difficulties which can be experienced arising from the different motivations and objectives in academic and industrial organisations.

Some companies have found it desirable to relocate their R&D laboratories to allow close contact with those working at the frontiers of technologies of vital concern for the future. For example, Pharmacia in Sweden moved its laboratory to be near Upsalla University, and Hewlett Packard has established R&D facilities close to Edinburgh and Stuttgart Universities. In some cases this has led to a concentration of companies in the same area to facilitate the exchange of personnel and expertise. This also applies to manufacturing, and many European and Japanese companies have established some of their production in Silicon Valley in the USA in the belief that this is the only effective way of tapping into the centre of electronic excellence. Distance may have little effect upon formal communication in today's world, but it can present a major barrier to the all-important informal contacts. The fact that some of the world's most successful companies have considered it essential to move physical facilities in order to improve the transfer of technology suggests that this is a policy which should be carefully considered.

Research and the authors' own observations support the conclusion that it is the world's most successful companies which have developed the widest range of arrangements, both formal and informal, with outside organisations, including competitors. In contrast, less successful firms are often more insular and inclined to delude themselves that there is little they can learn from others.

Technical change is dependent upon the acquisition of knowledge within a managerial framework. Amongst the questions a company should ask when considering its own position are:

- How do we currently identify potential sources of new technology?
  (a) Is this an actively managed process or is it left to chance?
  (b) How can we improve this process?
- Which are the most important sources of new knowledge?
  (a) How do we gain access to these sources?

(b) Do we encourage external contacts?

(c) Do we have a system for monitoring developments?

(d) Do any of our management systems, e.g. financial sanctioning or payment, discourage this activity?

(e) How can these barriers be removed?

- Who are our technical gatekeepers?

(a) How do we identify and use them?

(b) In what ways might our current practices discourage them?

(c) How can we widen the gatekeeper role to encourage greater participation?

- How is new knowledge transferred into our organisation?

(a) Where do major problems occur?

(b) How can these problems be removed?

(c) Are responsibilities clearly defined?

(d) Are training needs clearly identified?

(e) Is the training function involved at the planning stage?

- Have we analysed alternative systems for the transfer: recruitment, licensing, joint ventures, relocation of facilities, etc.?

- Is our outlook too insular and do we underrate what we can learn from others?

Generation of ideas

So far we have considered in isolation the two streams of information, technological and user needs, which must be married to provide the basis for an effective technical change. This can be achieved in three ways:

- the search for a technical solution to a clearly established need;
- the search for a useful application of a specific technical advance;
- the creative marriage of technology and user needs to develop a new potential for profit generation.

There are two general approaches running through this process. The first is the systematic analysis leading to the solution of a well-specified need or problem. The second is the imaginative leap to produce combinations which challenge the accepted wisdom and orthodoxy. The sytematic analysis, although some creativity is usually present, is more likely to lead to incremental change. In contrast, those ideas which are highly creative are likely to lead to radical proposals of greater potential value to the company provided they are able to satisfy more formal criteria subsequently. It is this creative aspect we shall now discuss.

Figure 5.3 illustrates how the ideas can evolve. In the first stage we have

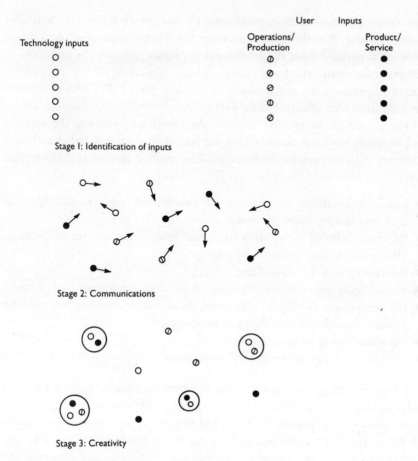

Fig. 5.3 Knowledge and creativity

the identification of user needs and technical potential as separate activities. The next stage is the bringing together of these two streams of knowledge, which is dependent upon effective internal communications. But it is only in the final stage that ideas for technical change are generated by the combinations, which we term creativity and which can occur in a random fashion. The Flymo lawnmower can be considered as an example. Its success was dependent upon the user need attributes of ease of operation through low friction and lack of physical contact with the lawn combined with the technological potential provided by the hovercraft or ground effect principle. This was a creative marriage and, whilst it is easy to comprehend the reasons for its success after the event, it is doubtful whether any process of rational analysis would have led to the identification of this opportunity. It is essentially a human occurrence that cannot be planned. Nevertheless, management can and should consider how they can create an environment conducive to this creative process. It is also worth noting that the exploitation of the Flymo was dependent upon another departure from the traditional approach, namely the adoption of rotary rather than cylindrical cutters. This is typical of what is commonly found in practice; the requirement to consider the total system in relation to a creative idea affecting only part of it.

The nature of the creative process, the creative person and the creative organisation has been described by the author in greater detail elsewhere.[5] Here we shall summarise the findings. The creative process is characterised by:

- new combinations or patterns of existing or new knowledge and concepts arising from the imagination;
- the association of ideas, often from widely different spheres of learning, which enable new patterns to emerge;
- the redefinition of a problem;
- mutual stimulation between people of different intellectual backgrounds;
- the temporary freeing of the mind from the constraints imposed by normal logical, rational thought processes;
- the questioning of assumptions;
- avoidance of premature critical evaluation.

All human beings are creative, but the term is usually applied to those who exhibit it to an above average extent. Although it is dangerous to generalise, their personalities often lead to patterns of behaviour which are different from those of their colleagues. Their work patterns can be unorthodox, they may resent conforming to the company's norms and procedures and they may be intolerant of the views of others. In short, they do not 'fit in'. In Chapter 2 we referred to one company which recognised the need for more creativity, but when senior managers were asked to describe the characteristics of a creative person they admitted that such a person would not be tolerated in their firm.

The motivations of creative people may also be different from those of their colleagues. In one research programme[6] where people deemed to be creative were asked to rank ten factors of importance in a creative organisation, the number of times each of them was cited as one of the two most important items were as follows:

Freedom to work on areas of greatest interest	44
Recognition and appreciation	41
Broad contacts with stimulating colleagues	38
Encouragement to take risks	26
Tolerance of non-conformity	12

Monetary rewards	8
Opportunity to work alone	3
Creativity training programmes	2
Criticism by supervisors and associates	1
Regular performance appraisals	0

Although this order of priorities might appear to suggest that creative people should be given a free hand to follow their own inclinations, a situation few companies would be prepared to tolerate, other research indicates that creativity is more likely to flourish in an environment which is managed but participative, rather than one of *laissez faire*.

The rewards a person obtains from his or her employment are personal satisfaction, organisational recognition and money. All three are important, but management should appreciate that the relative needs of creative people do differ from those of most other people in the organisation and they must tailor their policies towards them accordingly. These include:

- an acceptance of the need for creative people;
- a recognition of what motivates them;
- a management style that enables them to develop their creative skills within an environment which maintains managerial control associated with understanding and sensitivity to their requirements.

Creativity is also needed for the application of technology in the solution of problems which are well formulated. The obvious answers are not necessarily the best. The aim should be to seek a variety of possible solutions, including some which may be unorthodox, rather than to be satisfied with the first that comes to mind. Although the creative process described earlier may apply in these cases, assistance can also be provided by the use of creative problem-solving techniques which have been developed in recent years and used with success by a number of firms. These techniques fall into two classes: analytical and non-analytical. Analytical approaches include attribute analysis, morphological analysis, needs research and technology monitoring. The non-analytical or imagination-spurring techniques include brainstorming, synectics and lateral thinking. These techniques can be useful in both routine problem solving and the generation of ideas for entirely new applications of technology or the meeting of user needs.

The considerations we have discussed raise the following questions which should be addressed by managers:

- Is our company as creative as its competitors?
  (a) If not, why not?

(b) Does the lack of creativity hinder our performance?
- How can we create an environment conducive to creativity?
- Who are our most creative people?
  (a) Do we encourage or hinder them?
  (b) Can we identify managerial barriers to the exercise of creativity?
  (c) Do we reward people for their creative ideas?
  (d) How can we remove the barriers and provide the rewards that such people regard as important?
- Should we explore the possibility of employing creativity-spurring techniques?

Evaluating technical change proposals

There ought to be no shortage of ideas for change in any company. If there is, this is a strong indication that the processes of technology capture, identification of needs and creativity are deficient. As we have stressed earlier, these are dependent upon corporate culture, managerial style and organisational structure. Thus any shortcomings are unlikely to be overcome without top management involvement. Attention to the detailed procedures may effect some improvement, but will not solve the problem in the wrong corporate environment.

When there is an effective system for generating ideas for change, management is faced with making choices, for there are likely to be far more proposals than there are resources to support them. It is at this stage that a more formal and systematic approach is essential. A method for evaluation and selection is needed. However, in order to make an evaluation there must be an explicit set of criteria against which any proposal can be assessed. In doing this there are three main considerations:
- *Strategic.* Is the proposal consistent with the corporate strategy for both the short and the long term? How does it relate to the company's expressed desire to develop new products, reduce operational costs or improve managerial efficiency?
- *Portfolio.* How does it relate to existing activities or other programmes for technical change?
- *The project itself.* What are its intrinsic merits?

Strategic considerations

The existence of a corporate strategy might be taken to imply that all proposals for change will conform to it. This is by no means always the case, and there is much evidence that strategy formulation and operational decision making often occur on different planes. Strategy is concerned with the big issues, is often focused on trends and events outside the company, and may be confined to top and senior management unless it is communicated widely within the company. The authors frequently come across cases where operational managers have been given no indications of the company's strategic priorities. In this situation operational decisions, often involving technical change, are made in relation to departmental objectives isolated from the strategic interests of the company. Sometimes the reward system encourages actions which are in conflict with the strategy even when it has been communicated.

This lack of integration between strategic considerations and technical change can manifest itself in a variety of ways. Two examples will be quoted. In one conglomerate there was an active policy of acquisition, with some parts of the acquired companies being absorbed into the core businesses. The companies within the core businesses were set ambitious targets for profit growth, with their surpluses used by the parent company to fund its acquisition policy. All investment required head-office sanction, which was rarely given. As a consequence organic growth slowed, R&D was severely curtailed, morale was low and they faced long-term decline, which first affected their profitability and eventually their cash generation. This may be an extreme case, where top management was largely divorced from the operations, had little concern for the operations of its core businesses, inhibited technical change and eventually suffered from their inability to support the corporate aspirations.

An example of what happens more frequently is provided by companies which have invested in new manufacturing technology. Voss[7] quotes the results of a survey of 30 organisations involved in the implementation of advanced manufacturing technology. In only a few were the selection and design of the systems made in relation to business objectives such as quality or responsiveness to the market. Even in these cases they were managed in relation to technical objectives, and in a number of examples the technical control criteria were in direct conflict with the business objectives. This would appear to be one of the main reasons why managements often express dissatisfaction with the results of their investment in new technology.

There are a number of explanations of why top management and technical people fail to communicate effectively. In some companies the top management is dominated by people who have little understanding of technical matters. In many others the technical people have a poor appreciation of business criteria. Top management, with their broader concerns, take into account many criteria which are difficult to quantify, whereas technologists tend to stress the tangible and quantifiable measures. It has been noted earlier that a feature of successful innovative companies is the high volume of communication both downwards and upwards. Whilst this is an essential feature it is not sufficient if the communications are in language which the receivers do not fully understand. Thus a prerequisite for a successful technical change must be that it is selected in relation to strategic considerations which are fully understood by those responsible for implementing it and that this is not lost sight of as the project advances. This is one of the most common causes of failure. It cannot be overcome by the establishment of a communication system unless attention is focused on the managerial, attitudinal and educational factors which are essential if the system is to work effectively.

Portfolio considerations

The whole is greater than the sum of the parts. Rarely is a technical change freestanding, for two reasons. First, it usually forms part of a system where a change in one element can yield benefits to the company only if changes are introduced elsewhere. Secondly, it requires resources which would otherwise be available for some other purpose.

One company made a large investment in automated equipment to introduce a 'just in time' (JIT) system in manufacturing largely to eliminate work in progress between processes in its production department. Calculations of the inventory savings were used to justify the investment, which was duly reflected in a reduced unit cost of manufacture. However, when the effect of this change was examined the following was revealed. The major inventory costs were concentrated in expensive raw materials which the supplier would provide only in large batches, and in finished goods which accumulated at the end of the production line until they could be incorporated in the finished product. The elimination of the work in progress had merely moved the inventory investment to the two ends of the production line, with no total saving to the company. The investment had been justified in relation to the objectives of one department concerned with part of a system without any consideration of its impact elsewhere; other changes would have been necessary to yield a saving for the company. In order to reap the benefits of the JIT system an assessment of the effect upon the whole of the physical flows, including suppliers and customers, would have been needed.

It has also been noted that the introduction of JIT by one company has often been accompanied by increased inventories held by suppliers; in one case a supplier had to construct an enlarged warehouse. These factors cannot be ignored, since increased supplier costs are, in the long term, likely to be reflected in their prices. Thus what may start as a simple technical change may involve a wide range of other departments, including a revision of purchasing relationships, if its benefits are to be fully exploited. As a consequence a fundamental review of the organisation of the flow of work throughout the system may be required in order to achieve the desired degree of integration.

At any point in time there will be a portfolio of products being offered to the market and a portfolio of developments to maintain or extend it. In the case of the products, some of them may share components, they may be mutually supportive in that a number of products are required to cover the whole of the market, they will be at different stages in their product lives, and they will share marketing resources. The removal or addition of, or change to, one constituent affects the total either because they are mutually supportive or because they share resources. Similar considerations apply to new product development. Whilst the aim must be to support the market portfolio, there is the additional element of uncertainty and its associated risk to be taken into account when the developments involve new technology or a radically different product. As with an investment portfolio, it is the performance of the whole that is important. There will be some high-risk but potentially highly rewarding constituents and others with lower but more stable expectations. A balance must be struck.

Thus in considering any technical change it is necessary to compare the expected RoI of the total portfolio before and after the change rather than consider its merits in isolation. In some cases this may result in the rejection of a proposal which otherwise might be regarded as highly desirable. This complicates the decision-making process because it is much more difficult to quantify the impact on the total portfolio than the individual proposals, since it often introduces factors which are difficult to express in quantitative terms. Nevertheless, the attempt must be made.

The initiator of a proposal is likely to be concerned solely with its intrinsic merits. He or she has a narrow view and may not appreciate either the portfolio or strategic considerations which can affect its desirability in relation to the business as a whole. To some extent this is inevitable, but an organisation that does not attempt to involve the initiator in the decision-making process or to explain the wider context of the criteria used is likely to demotivate him or her and discourage him or her from initiating proposals in the future.

The proposal itself

Notwithstanding the considerations discussed above, a detailed evaluation of the intrinsic merits of any proposal for technical change must be undertaken. A formal system is essential in order to impose upon the proposer the need for a rigorous justification. Ideally this would result in an estimate of the financial benefits in relation to the company's normal investment criteria. However, as discussed in Chapter 3, the uncertainties involved in innovation make this a dubious exercise if too much reliance is placed upon a simple financial evaluation, although this must remain an important element of the evaluation process. Many aspects of the evaluation must of necessity be judgemental, but must include the following considerations:

- strategic;
- marketing (or user benefits);
- research and development;
- financial, including risk assessment;
- operational (i.e. production or service);
- personnel;
- training.

A checklist incorporating a number of factors under each of these headings is often found to be of great value.

Whilst it must be recognised that no evaluation system can guarantee success, it is essential in order to ensure that:

- All relevant factors having a bearing on the total business implications of the proposal are examined explicitly.
- A discipline is imposed on those involved to ensure they carry out a detailed justification.
- The critical factors for success (or failure) are identified.
- The need for additional information is revealed.
- There is a common basis for comparing proposals.
- There is a procedure for obtaining information and commitment from all those affected by the change.
- Assumptions are recorded for future reference.

In some cases the evaluation process will lead to a rejection or will reveal serious deficiencies which require further investigation. However, if it appears attractive and work is initiated, this must still be regarded as a provisional approval, with further reviews being carried out to re-evaluate it periodically in the light of progress and the effect of additional information. Although the evaluation system is important as a decision-making tool, its greatest value can lie in its managerial aspects. It provides a mechanism for laying the foundations for the integration of the change into all the functions of the business that will be affected by it and involving them from an early stage.

Great care must be exercised in the choice and use of an evaluation system. Although formality is essential, over-sophistication of the techniques used can lead to the placing of too much weight on the manipulation of data, much of which is based on judgement in the early stage of a project. Furthermore, it must be recognised that the evaluation system acts as a filter; it creates nothing. Thus there is always the danger that the flow of ideas may be inhibited by a system which is applied too rigorously whilst major uncertainties remain. If the filter is too fine, few proposals are accepted; this in turn will inhibit the flow of ideas. Thus the system cannot be considered in isolation from its effect upon the behaviour of the people involved in it.

Example: *innovation programme of a European chemical company*
The innovation programme adopted by a major European chemical firm illustrates an integrated approach to the generation and evaluation of ideas for technical change. This company, in a mature industry, was experiencing a shortage of new product proposals. It decided to institute a programme to overcome this problem consisting of five stages:
Stage 1, concept generation. This involved over 200 employees using a variety of approaches including brainstorming, morphological analysis and Delphi studies. This resulted in the generation of over 700 ideas.
Stage 2, idea screening. A preliminary screening of the ideas was undertaken using three criteria:

- reasonableness;
- known or unknown;
- worthy of consideration.

This reduced the number of ideas considered worthy of further consideration to approximately 100.
Stage 3, relevance to the company. The remaining ideas were then categorised in relation to how well they fitted the corporate strategy as it existed at that time (two thirds of the ideas), or as it might be in the future (one third). It was accepted that some of the ideas might be of sufficient merit to warrant a modification to the strategy, but in such cases they would need to offer exceptional benefits.
Stage 4, evaluation. The ideas were then submitted to the company's formal evaluation procedure and those satisfying the criteria were allocated priorities.
Stage 5, project selection. A few proposals were then selected for development in relation to their fit with the R&D and market portfolios and the availability of resources.

At first sight this may appear an expensive and wasteful process, since only a few of the 700 original ideas were developed into commercial products. However, it did result in products which would not have been developed otherwise and was judged by the company to have been well worth the effort devoted to it.

The example of the European chemical company reflects a structured approach to encouraging creativity within the context of a formal system.

Striking the right balance between creating the innovative environment and the procedures for evaluation is critical for success. This is illustrated by the experience of two competing companies in the food industry. In the first there was a highly sophisticated system for managerial evaluation and control of new product development. Their problem was a shortage of proposals, which they rationalised as a characteristic of their industry: 'How can we identify new foods in an activity where there has been human experience since Eve offered Adam the apple?'. A short creativity session came up with ideas, but did not solve their dilemma. The product development manager of the second company described his difficulty to the author quite differently: 'Everybody eats; how can I select which products to develop from the continuous stream of ideas I receive from my staff?'. These two companies had opposite perceptions of the character of the food industry. In fact their contrasting experiences were a reflection of the company cultures: one had rigid systems which inhibited the generation of ideas, whereas the other possessed an innovative environment but lacked the formal procedures for evaluation and selection. This raises important questions that management should consider:

- Is my perception of the characteristics of my industry a reflection of reality?
- Do other companies in the industry see it the same way?
- Is this perception a consequence of the relative importance we give to the encouragement of creativity in comparison with formal procedures?

Technical change design

The processes described so far lead to the generation of the concept for a technical change and its evaluation, leading to a decision to proceed. This is a relatively inexpensive exercise, but is the vital ingredient for success. A high-quality concept may succeed in spite of shortcomings in its detailed design and development. A poor concept will fail however well it is executed.

Design is normally a technical responsibility. It should be carried out to a specification which states clearly the objectives in terms of technical performance, cost and timing, which must reflect the user requirements it is aimed at satisfying. The specification is essential for the work of the design team, but it can also have the effect of isolating them from the rest of the organisation whilst the project progresses. This often sows the seeds for future trouble, in that:

- The designers may lose sight of the business objectives due to their preoccupation with the technicalities.
- There is never one ideal solution, but a choice of alternatives depending upon the weights attached to the user attributes. The designers are likely to stress the technical performance attributes, thereby leading to a design which fails to meet other user needs such as cost, ease of maintenance or aesthetic appeal.
- The needs of implementation may be neglected. A product may be difficult or expensive to manufacture, a process may demand unavailable skills, or a management system may be incompatible with other systems.
- Changes can occur in user needs or business objectives which are not appreciated by the designers and thus not reflected in their design.
- Technical difficulties may lead to modifications being introduced without due consideration of their effect upon the business or the user.

For these reasons it is not uncommon for a technical change design to emerge from development which, although meeting its technical specification, fails to satisfy fully its business or market objectives. This is more likely to occur in a hierarchical organisation based upon the division of labour and arm's length relationships. It must be recognised, however, that in spite of the fact that a specification may be detailed, there will be times when it requires interpretation in relation to many non-technical considerations. This process is facilitated by an integrated organisation of the type discussed in Chapter 4.

There is one other factor we have not discussed so far. That is the perceived risk to the user. The greater the change from what users are familiar with, the greater they perceive the risk to be. Some of this will be genuine, stemming from the uncertainties inherent in new technology, and is unavoidable. But much of it results from distrust of the unfamiliar, and may not be soundly based. The design of the change can do much to allay these fears. The language used to describe the technology and its physical appearance can play an important part in this. Thus the early car was called a 'horseless carriage' and had many of the characteristics of a carriage. Although this was to a large extent dictated by the state of the technology at the time, there is little doubt that this made it more acceptable than would have been a product called a motorcar and designed as such. Designers must be aware of these considerations and attempt so far as is possible to minimise these understandable user fears, perhaps by planning to introduce over time a series of smaller changes of increasing sophistication even though it may be feasible to introduce them all at the outset.

Making it happen

No technical change is of any value until it is fully implemented. It is not sufficient to 'do the right thing'; it must also be 'done right'. This is a function of change management. We shall now discuss some of the considerations relevant to effective project management. The behavioural and organisational implications are discussed in other chapters.

The project champion

Analysis of successful technical change programmes frequently reveals the existence of one key individual: the technical champion, technical entre-preneur or intrapreneur. This is a person who is committed to an idea for technical change, even though it may not be his or her own idea, and who is determined to see its introduction. Often the project champion will force it through in spite of strong resistance elsewhere in the organisation, perhaps risking his or her career in the process.

It must be appreciated that there will always be opposition to any proposal for change. This can arise from the lack of a company culture which favours innovation, from the reluctance most people show to changes affecting them which they have not originated themselves, or from a genuine threat to their power or influence, or even their job. Thus any suggestion for change is unlikely to be readily accepted, particularly if it means a radical innovation, for a number of reasons, some rational and some emotional. Since change involves uncertainty and risk, it is always possible to advance judgements to ensure that it will not satisfy the rigid interpretation of evaluation criteria. Although it might appear unprofessional, all change programmes require an element of faith and enthusiasm for success, for it is difficult to prove conclusively that a change is desirable; however, it is easy to find reasons for rejecting it on the grounds of uncertainty or timing.

Thus one finds that change is unlikely to occur without the intervention of an individual dedicated to it and determined to force it through in the face of opposition. If the resistance is too strong there will be no change. If the resistance is weak the company can be faced with changes forced upon it without adequate justification. These arguments might appear to suggest that the champion is needed only in non-innovative companies. This is not so. The most innovative firms, for example 3M, recognise the importance of this role, actively encourage champions, and structure their organisations to facilitate it. This does not imply that there should be a state of corporate anarchy, with the support of every champion. Whilst the enthusiasm and the commitment of the champion are vital ingredients, these must be wedded to a detailed justification for a change proposal. There must be a balance, but in the final analysis such companies rate highly the contribution of the individual.

Champions need not be technologists. They can be users, marketing people or members of top management. What is important is that they have commitment and the ability to push the idea through the organisation and carry it through to completion.

The project manager

It should not be assumed that all technical change occurs through the intervention of a champion facing organisational resistance. There are many changes that are introduced as an act of corporate policy, although the ideas may have originated at a low level in the company. In such cases it is necessary to appoint a project manager to bring the change to fruition.

One could postulate an ideal project which is completely planned in advance. The specification lays down all aspects of the design. A sophisticated planning and control system details the work to be carried out, allocates resources, measures progress, shows variances and indicates where corrective action is necessary. The project moves steadily to a successful conclusion monitored by management. In practice this does not occur, for a number of reasons:

- *The needs change.* With the passage of time new knowledge of user needs or the actions of competitors necessitates the introduction of modifications.
- *Unforeseen difficulties.* These can take a variety of forms. There may be technical problems in development or implementation, the company's cash flow may dictate a rescheduling, suppliers may fail to deliver on time, or there may be labour problems.
- *Avoidable problems.* Difficulties are bound to be experienced due to human errors which, although they should not occur, will always happen because of human fallibility.

Thus the project must be actively managed in order to allocate resources and instil a sense of urgency. It demands a person who understands the totality of the project in relation to its business objectives, who is dedicated to its success, and who is in control of the resources needed to achieve the end result. Whilst a good planning and control system is essential, it can only provide a framework for decision making and supply the information required for managerial intervention. The greater the degree of change from normal practice, the greater the number of variations from the plan and the greater the demand upon management.

Because there is an urgent need for remedial action it cannot be left to the deliberations of a committee. This is the rationale for a system of project management which enables one person to take timely decisions with the minimum of interference. This person's position is analogous with that of the champion, but whereas the champion assumes the role him or herself, the project manager is appointed to implement a change which has already received the support of management.

The need for urgency

In Chapter 3 we noted the influence of project delay upon profitability; it was noted that an increase in development cost may have a relatively insignificant effect. We shall now discuss how these considerations affect the managerial decisions taken during a technical change programme.

Figure 5.4 shows a typical cumulative cash flow diagram for a technical project. It can be divided into three phases: design, development and implementation. The important point to note is the rapid escalation of cost between the stages, something that many managements seriously under-

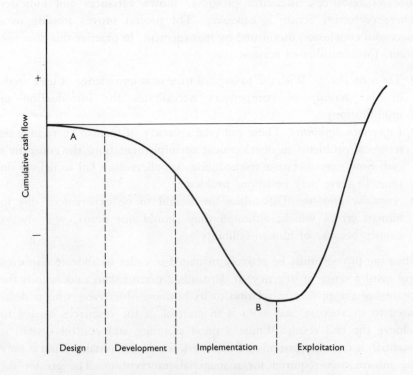

A, B: Periods where project duration is most sensitive to management action

Fig. 5.4 Technical change: cumulative cash flow curve

estimate, although they may have a general appreciation of it. For some new products the ratios may be as high as 1:10:100. In particular it is the high cost of implementation which may not be fully recognised, leading to higher programme costs than estimated, affecting project profitability, possibly causing cash flow problems for a large project, and in new venture companies being a common explanation for their business failure.

The cash flow diagram is the consequence of all the decisions made by management during the course of the change programme. Thus, within limits, it can be reshaped by modifying the decisions. An examination of the shape of the curve indicates that the total project duration can be reduced most cheaply at the two ends. At the beginning there is often a lack of a sense of urgency. The design (or applied research) phase can be reduced by the allocation of additional resources and by tight management. In some cases it might be advantageous to carry out alternative explorations of a problem in parallel; this, although wasteful, can often be justified in relation to a possible reduction in the time to find an answer. It must be stressed, however, that we are considering a compression of this stage by spending more money; it does not imply that it should be curtailed by leaving essential design or planning to a later stage in the programme.

Towards the end of the programme the major investment has been made, but it is not earning any return, yet the flattening of the curve is characteristic of most programmes. There are a number of reasons for this. The manager may be removed to a new project where his or her skills are required, thereby introducing changeover problems and a loss of urgency. Frequently there are delays for such diverse reasons as the training of staff, trivial remedial or finishing work (e.g. painting) or the preparation of service manuals. For whatever reason, this delay represents the loss of earning capacity from a large investment.

There is one other method for reducing project time, although it can involve a greater element of risk; this is the carrying out in parallel of activities which are normally sequential. Thus it might be decided to proceed with the installation of a manufacturing plant before the product design is frozen. The risk is that it may have to be modified later or, at worst, may have to be scrapped if the project has to be abandoned. An increasing number of companies are today accepting these risks and additional costs in order to reap the benefits of an earlier completion date.

Planning and control systems

Planning and control systems are concerned with the allocation of resources and the provision of information to enable corrective action to be taken when necessary. Many sophisticated, often computer-based, systems are now available and widely used. Since a detailed description is beyond the scope of this book, we shall merely note a few important considerations:

- Any change should be planned in as much detail as is realistic in relation to the nature of the change.
- The system used should be flexible so that plans can be modified quickly to accept new information. This may mean that information systems used for routine operations are often unsuitable without modification.
- Contingency plans should be drawn up where there are major uncertainties.
- The system must be comprehensive and include all factors relevant to its introduction throughout the business.
- It should provide only that information required by the decision maker in a form that can be easily assimilated and at the time it is needed.

Important questions for management in respect of the implementation of a change programme are:

- Do we recognise the role of the champion in bringing about technical change?
  - (a) Who are our champions?
  - (b) Do we encourage or discourage them?
  - (c) How can we improve our use of champions?
- Do we appoint project managers?
  - (a) If so, do they have responsibility for *all* aspects of implementation?
  - (b) Are they really the managers of their projects or merely information coordinators without the power to take decisions?
- Do we recognise the need for urgency?
  - (a) Can we identify where additional resources can effectively 'buy time'?
  - (d) Do we know the shape of a typical cash flow curve and understand its implications?
- Do we plan in sufficient detail before initiating action?
  - (a) Is the planning and control system appropriate for technical change?
  - (b) Is it flexible?
  - (c) Does it provide the right information at the right time?

Summary

In this chapter we have considered a number of key factors for the generation of ideas for technical change and their effective translation into practice. Figure 5.5 is a diagrammatic illustration of the interactions between these elements, namely:

- an innovative corporate environment reflected in its culture, organisation and strategy;
- the identification, capture and transfer of technological knowledge;
- the identification of the needs of the users and their involvement in the change programme in so far as is feasible;
- creativity to generate the ideas and the encouragement of a creative corporate environment;
- the integration of the change throughout the business and the early involvement of all functions affected by it;
- the emergence of a champion or the appointment of a project manager to drive the change through to a successful conclusion;
- the sensitive use of formal management systems for evaluation, specification and planning and control, to impose a discipline on the programme without inhibiting the flow of ideas or frustrating the project manager.

The existence of these factors cannot guarantee success. Nevertheless, the absence of one or more of them is characteristic of the majority of unsuccessful change programmes.

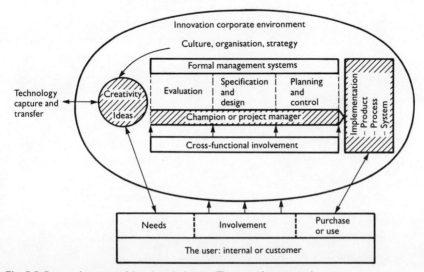

Fig. 5.5 Factors for successful technical change: 'The egg of innovation'

References

1. Von Hippel, E. (1987) Has a customer already developed your new product? In Roberts, E. B. (ed.) *Generating Technological Innovation*. Oxford University Press.
2. Peters, T. J. and Waterman, R. H. (1982) *In Search of Excellence*. Harper and Row.
3. Davis, P. and Wilkof, K. (1988) Scientific technical information transfer. *R&D Management* **18**(1), Jan.
4. Harvey-Jones, Sir J. (1988) *Making it Happen: Reflections on Leadership*. Collins.
5. Twiss, B. C. (1986) *Managing Technological Innovation*, 3rd edition. Pitman.
6. Parmeter, S. M. and Garber, J. D. (1971) Creative scientists rate creativity factors. *Research Management*, November.
7. Voss, C. A. (1986) Implementing manufacturing technology: a manufacturing strategy approach. *International Journal of Operations and Production Management*, **6**(4).

6 Strategies for managing change

In this chapter we shall look at some of the means by which organisations have successfully managed technological change. We have made reference many times in this book to the need to adopt specific management strategies for implementing change, as so many of our existing strategies are appropriate only for managing the status quo.

Technological change can occur in major leaps or incremental steps. Both require careful management to be executed effectively.

There are no generally accepted blueprints or prescriptions about managing the introduction of new technology. There are plenty of anecdotes, plenty of examples of success and failure, but no universally regarded techniques. Some of the results can make depressing reading: escalating costs, time delays and poor market acceptance of final products. Many of these issues we have already addressed. Studies of information technology implementation[1] have frequently concluded that most attempts at innovation yield 'working non-solutions'; the technical side works but somehow it does not fit the organisation's needs. A US study[1] of 2000 firms revealed that 40 per cent of computer-based information systems failed to satisfy the user's requirements. Other studies have concluded that this level of failure is due to organisational behaviour problems that arise during the design and implementation.

We can look at new technology in organisations as having three components:

- innovative technology;
- the context into which it is being introduced;
- the process for embedding that technology into the organisation.

Studies of success and failure converge on the former two components for explaining why some projects work and others do not. The purpose of this chapter is to examine the third component.

Is managing technological change different?

In a recent study on innovation[2] chief executive officers of nearly 1000 organisations in the USA, Europe and Japan were asked about the inno-

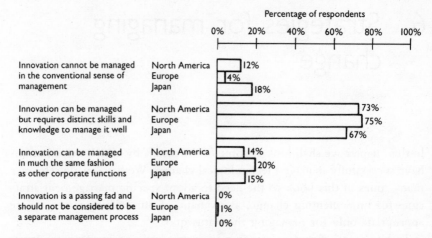

Fig. 6.1 Senior management perceptions on the management of innovation. *Source*: Little, A. D. (1985) *Management Perspectives on Innovation.*

vation process. Their opinions are shown in Fig. 6.1. The overwhelming view in all three regions was that innovation can be managed, but that it requires distinct skills and knowledge to manage it well. The skills and knowledge required we shall return to in Chapter 7.

One of the pitfalls of seeing the management of innovation too separately from the 'normal' management process is that it suggests that managing innovation is a transitory process to arrive at a new equilibrium or steady state. There are periods in any organisation of faster and slower change, but it can never become static. All the evidence suggests that the pace of change is accelerating and therefore we have a continuum from constant and habitual incremental improvement of everything we do *all the time* to major step changes in technology at less frequent intervals. The innovation cycle has no beginning and no end in the company which is to survive successfully. The only question is the balance of resource and management effort between maintaining the existing and developing and bringing forward the new.

The greenfield site

One way of avoiding many of the organisational change issues is to bed new technologies in new organisations in new physical locations. Where there are major leaps in technology the setting up of an entirely new facility removed from previous facilities has considerable advantages. Where capital expenditure for the new facility is high, the process is new and there are few pieces of old technology which can be used to support the new, then it becomes particularly attractive to set up a greenfield site. EMI music set up their compact disc plant in Swindon on a new industrial estate. The product was new and the process for its production was a radical departure from the manufacture of black vinyl records and cassette tapes, which is carried out in west London. Similarly, when GKN set up their composite fibre spring plant in Telford, it was well removed from any of their other production plants.

The advantages of the greenfield site option can be summarised as follows:

- no disruption of existing operations;
- purpose-built premises;
- opportunity to build a new culture;
- free hand in recruitment.

Psychologically it provides a break with the past. Attitudes do not have to be changed. We recruit those who have the aptitude and the attitude to optimise the new process. We are unencumbered by custom and practice, trade unions and fossilised company systems.

One major UK-based electronics company has given up trying to change existing organisations, factories and management teams. Instead it places all new products and processes in greenfield sites and in this way few obstacles remain from the inheritance of the organisational past. This is a depressing conclusion. Why is it that organisations are so difficult to change? In all the above cases it was perfectly feasible to place the investment in existing sites, and in many cases it would have been cheaper, but the transitional problems were felt to be too great.

It is an important conclusion if companies are beginning to see technological change in terms of a major organisational hiatus. In other words, to be successful we have to literally bulldoze the old and create the new elsewhere. It is interesting to reflect on the new companies setting up in the decayed industrial heartlands of the UK. One of the major reasons for the decay is often felt to be the failure of the indigenous companies to change, embrace different technologies, and so on. Yet the very people whom we felt were so unadaptable now run the lines at Nissan in Sunderland and the electronics companies around Glasgow, exhibiting behaviour patterns which their previous managers would have considered impossible.

Example
Of three companies on an industrial estate in Scotland, the first, an engineering company manufacturing precision components, has recruited all its skilled labour from the heavy engineering companies on Clydeside. The company is non-union, everyone is

fully flexible, productivity is high and the culture belies the origins of its workforce. The second is a major electronics company, also non-unions; many of the workforce are female, productivity is high, and the plant has adapted and responded to many major technological changes. The third plant employs both males and females. Productivity is average, flexibility is poor and the management believe that both are a function of their location and the attitude to work in their recruitment catchment area.

There has to be some reason for these major differences in performance. What can be said about the first two companies is that they are both able to manage change, actively motivate their workforce and are undimmed by the history of the region. They have had the advantage of setting up afresh in the last 15 years, but have sustained that difference. If the culture is so pervasive then how can such different styles and approaches coexist so closely with employees recruited from the same villages and families?

Changing existing organisations

We shall concentrate primarily upon changing existing organisations rather than the greenfield site option. Many of the points we make are equally true if we are to manage the introduction of technology in a green-field site; however, not having to concern oneself with the baggage of the past is a distinct advantage.

Successful management of change requires a combination of direct and indirect means (Fig. 6.2). The direct means are those we most commonly

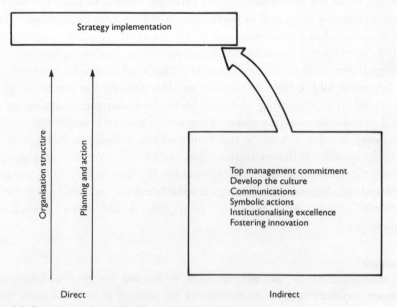

Fig. 6.2 Organisation change: the direct and indirect means

see as important in the rational side of management. These can be typified as follows:

- organisational structure;
- implementation planning and action.

These, however, will be effective only if they are combined with indirect strategies such as:

- gaining top management commitment;
- actively developing the corporate culture;
- communications;
- symbolic actions;
- institutionalising excellence;
- fostering innovation.

It is the combination of the two, with each item and action reinforcing all the others, that leads to the successful implementation of technological change (Fig. 6.3).

We shall take each in turn. Particular emphasis will be placed upon the indirect means, as these are the items which are often, and can most easily be, left out and forgotten.

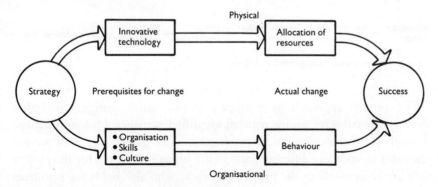

Fig. 6.3 The key components of managing technological change

The direct means of managing innovation

Organisation structure

Technological change is complex and its implications far-reaching, and as we have seen it requires a different approach to the way in which we manage much of our day-to-day activity. It is for this reason that we put great emphasis on 'projects', 'project managers' and 'champions'. Change processes do not seem to be effectively managed through functionalised or indeed centralised management structures; they are best managed as projects with clear objectives and clear boundaries, and managed overall by one person who has the competence and the commitment to make the change happen. Coupled with this we have to ensure that the project manager or project champion has the power and resources to deliver the objective. When speaking of the competent manager who can manage change we think of the project manager. Those who have the burning commitment to see it work we shall call the project champions.

We have found relatively few companies with a clear idea of how they wish to manage technological change. Too often it follows an *ad hoc* sequence, with the previous department being blamed for the non-performance of the department with current responsibility for the project (see Goodridge, J. M. and Twiss, B. (1988) *Technology, Management and Change*, Training Agency.) (Fig. 6.4). In this case, only the highest levels of management can be seen to have overall responsibility, and even that can be a vague and woolly concept. So often in our research we find groups of managers saying that they are responsible for the technology, others for the costs, and still others for production, and so on. No one seems to have responsibility for pulling together the whole task.

Technology change → Research and development → Process/Product engineering → Design engineering → Project engineering → Operations → Personnel

Fig. 6.4 The sequential management of change

The project approach to managing technological change insists that there is one cohesive group with an identified manager who will manage through from development to production. The group may well second resources from many different parts of the organisation, but for the project they are responsible to the project manager, who also holds the resources (money, people and power) (Fig. 6.5).

For many people in organisations the process of technological change has been divorced from them. They have certainly seen the impact of it, often directly on their own working lives, but the processes of change have been the province of separately defined and directed organisational entities such as the planning, design and implementing departments; the combined results of which are 'dumped' at the feet of those who are required to make it all work. The 'externalisation' of change has meant that these processes are unfamiliar; people are unused to working with anything other than steady-state situations. In a sense the same is true for those in the external departments who are the instigators and architects

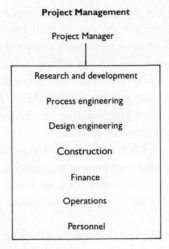

Project Management

Project Manager

Research and development

Process engineering

Design engineering

Construction

Finance

Operations

Personnel

Fig. 6.5 The integrated management of change

of technological change. Their steady state is the stream of 'new projects' which largely need to be processed in a common, albeit restricted, way.

Nadler and Robinson[3] observe that the organisation which is so structured promotes compartmentalised views of technological change. They rightly argue that the words 'planning, design and implementation' should be replaced by phrases such as 'continuing improvement' or 'habitual incremental improvement'. We need to consider how we can break down some of these functional barriers to promote effective change.

Organisation options

Between these two extremes of autonomous project management on the one hand and sequential management on the other there are many shades of grey. Usually this means that senior management wish to retain influence on resources, money and power. Unless the relationships are very clear then often confusion and muddle reign. One of the commonest issues is the assigning of project responsibility to an individual whilst expecting a full performance in that manager's normal job. Such arrangements inevitably lead to conflicting priorities and the dilemma as to which is more important: producing today's production quota or making one step towards a project completion in one year's time. It takes little to guess which will have the priority. It is most likely that we are able to measure today's quota and highly unlikely that we can measure the one step forward in the project. The crude management maxim 'You can only manage what you can measure' will undoubtedly prevail.

In all but the smallest projects it is essential to have a dedicated project manager with a clear objective, quantified resources and the unswerving support of at least one key senior manager. There is talks of the additional need for a sponsor. These are the one or two senior managers who have the clout and the commitment to protect the project manager and champion when the chips are down, the project is behind, the quality is poor, the materials wastage is far too high and the customers are screaming because the wonder product has been oversold by the sales team. Regrettably, in most organisations the fact that the board approved the project in the first place and understood the nature of the risk has rarely been a guarantee of wholehearted support when things start to go wrong. The disadvantage of having just one person responsible for the project is that it may seem that there is only one person to blame: this is another reason for strong sponsors who are as committed as the project champion him or herself.

One of the major constraints on the single project manager concept is the extent to which one individual can have the depth of knowledge of the technology coupled with the business breadth to see it through from R&D to production. In particularly complex situations it has therefore proven necessary to have a rolling team responsible for the project. In other words, a project manager from the research laboratory might take the team leadership through to final development and first prototypes, and then hand over the leadership to a more production-orientated manager, the first manager remaining in the team. This can be most effective if there is a commonality of purpose in the team and its members can act cohesively.

During the authors' visit to Hitachi Research and Development we were taken through the range of models which they use for creating teams to transfer technology from laboratories into new products and processes. This is not uncommon in Western research establishments. What was of considerable interest, however, was the extent to which these alternative models were known and understood in the production works as well as in the laboratories. Furthermore, team composition and membership were clearly understood, measures of performance agreed and detailed training undertaken for all team members.

Figure 6.6 shows four organisational models of transferring technology into the factory. Pattern A is the direct handing over of the technology from the laboratory to the works. This is done only where the transfer is straightforward and the technology relatively simple, and where the users have the need for the technology and are wholly convinced of its use and performance.

This model is the one which has so often proven inadequate for the more complex changes and represents what we have previously called the sequential or functional approach.

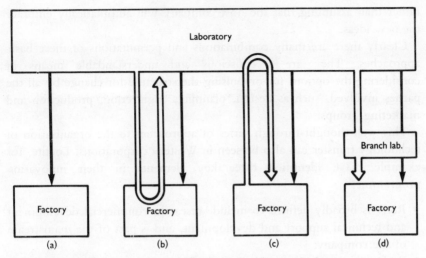

Fig. 6.6 Four organisational models of transferring technology into the factory

In Pattern B those who have been responsible for the development of the new product or process come and work in the works or factory to refine and implement. It may be that in the early stages the team is led by a project manager from the laboratories, who then hands the responsibility over to a manager from the works. Alternatively, the manager from the works may have responsibility right from the start. The joint team works together until implementation is completed successfully. On completion the development people return to their home base.

This model is increasingly being used by R&D functions in the UK as they become more customer orientated. Furthermore, it ensures that R&D people get integrated project management experience, gain credibility from operations management, and become closer to their ultimate customer.

Pattern C is where a small number of the intended users work in the laboratory or development group for the final stages of the development of the technology. This form is of particular use when the new product or process requires final refinement using end–user and customer knowledge and skills. Once the technology has been perfected then the combined team moves to the works, where implementation is integrated into the host organisation.

Pattern D is used where the total organisation is vast and often central R&D is remote; in this case there can be distinct advantages in transferring the technology to a group or individual development facility before final transfer to the host works. Again the method is one of bringing the technology closer to the customer and allowing integration to take place, rather than assuming that the host company will automatically embrace the new ideas.

Clearly there are many combinations and permutations of these basic approaches. They are a conscious and understandable means of considering the options for organising the structure for change by all the parties involved, such as design, planning, engineering, production and marketing groups.

This well thought-through series of approaches to the organisation of technology transfer can also be seen in Western corporations. Loctite, for example, have identified three key elements in their innovation programme:

- R&D is broadly defined to include research, commercial development and technical support and development, and is part of the mainstream of the company.
- R&D management participate in the business strategy process at both corporate and strategic business unit level.
- An R&D agenda is produced to ensure that innovation relates specifically to the goals and objectives identified by the strategy development process.

A very similar pattern is adopted by Eastman Kodak, where there is a two-way street of innovation. All functions have the responsibility to innovate and, conversely, R&D are involved in that innovation process wherever it takes place.

In both companies the role of R&D has changed from a passive to an active, if not dominant, role. Technical strategy is integrated into business strategy and the broad boundaries of the role ensure that they are involved right through to commercial exploitation and success.

Implementation planning and action

It is hard to reach an objective without knowing the route you are going to take. Planning provides us with that route and measurement with the knowledge of progress. There is abundant information on planning methods and techniques, some highly complex, others quite basic. None is perfect, and much rests on what is actually measurable. In a complex change process there is often a massive range of possible dimensions against which we can plan and measure. The difficulty here is often deciding which ones are critical and how progress along one dimension relates to progress along another. Furthermore, as we have seen, innovation is inherently risky and is peppered with uncertainty. How can we plan for this risk and uncertainty? By and large the answer is that we cannot.

A further complication to the planning process is that if we are to stand the highest chance of success we must deal with soft as well as hard data. The hard data are all the physical things we can measure: expenditure, physical progress, customer trials, pricing policy, and so on. The soft data are the intangibles: motivation of the project team, whether the research team is going to come up with that vital technical solution, the trade unions' reaction to a single-union agreement and flexible manning, and so on.

The planning question goes back to the overall purpose of the project team. Is it there to provide a technically competent solution or is it there to see that technical solution operate and deliver to cost a quality product? We believe it should be the latter, the implementation task explicitly defined and understood, and the team given the resources to achieve this aim. If we accept the latter then the planning process must take into account both the soft and the hard, the direct and the indirect, means of managing innovation.

Example

A very successful information technology consultancy group explained that they were in the business of providing solutions to the client's problems. On further questioning we found that a client's problem was as defined by the in-house IT group and that a solution was defined as something which met the technical specification. A golden rule in the group was not to get involved in implementation, for to do so was to open yourself up to the client's staff fouling up the system and the consultants getting the blame. An interesting prescription for the development of 'working non-solutions'.

The key is to shift from a totally technology-driven planning process to one which can embrace the social and organisational side of the equation. This can appear to many as a recipe for disaster and an excuse for sloppy planning and poor implementation, but the evidence is clear that the rational technical planning approach is defective. Project teams and project champions must have that broader role to embed the technology in the organisation rather than merely to present it to the organisation on a take-it-or-leave-it basis.

It is here that we need to distinguish between different forms and types of technological change. Information technology applications have proven particularly difficult to embed. We have already looked at failure rates and some of the prime reasons for those failures. Too many information technology systems are able to be bypassed and ignored by users and operators alike. Without full commitment it is difficult to see how the most technically superb solution can ever be effective.

With a new manufacturing process the break with the past is often more abrupt and there is less opportunity for those operating new processes to ignore the technology's requirements. Here again, without high degrees of competence and commitment, commissioning will be slow, problems will take a long time to sort out and profit will be lost.

Planning and decision-making processes which bring technology into existing organisations and workplaces need to be participative in nature if the social and technical systems are to be jointly optimised in relationship to the organisation's mission. Such approaches necessarily mean that innovation implementation must plan to include involvement by all those affected by the technology throughout the implementation process. The social and organisational issues will differ from one company to another, but into the technical plan we have to integrate our social, human resources and organisational plan (Fig. 6.7).

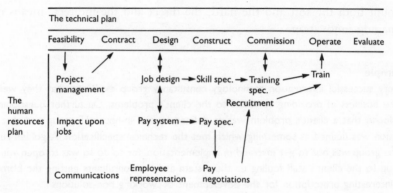

Fig. 6.7 Integrating the organisational issues into the project plan

To expect a project team to be addressing all these issues requires either much training or the co-option of experts. Either way the project team has to continue to negotiate its legitimacy in the company and the rental of resources, to communicate its purpose and actively manage the embedding of the technology such that it is embraced, made effective and owned by those who must use it to provide profit for the company.

Example
A UK snack-food manufacturer decided to introduce computerised weighing and packing equipment at the end of each line. The cost savings, through improved packing weight conformance and significant manpower reductions, were major. The engineering department bought a pilot set of equipment, placed it on a line and asked for volunteers to man it. None were forthcoming, so the engineering department manned it themselves, using temporary labour. At no time were the production management, let alone the employees, involved in the pilot study. The net result was that the line management said that the equipment would not work and the employees went on strike.

Advanced manufacturing systems stemming from manufacturing strategies are having to address all these issues. Chris Voss[5] analysed the articles in leading journals on the subject from the 1960s to 1983 to see how many have been concerned with implementation as opposed to the purely technical solution. Until 1976 hardly a word was mentioned on the subject; since then it has become a preoccupation, with the focus on implementation. This has led to the specialists who advise and assist companies in advanced manufacturing systems to develop planning frameworks which embody what we have called both direct and indirect means of technology implementation.

Arthur Young in the USA has developed a world-class manufacturing planning framework[5] which has enjoyed a high degree of success. The basic assumption that the framework is built upon is the fundamental interrelatedness of business strategy, information technology, manufacturing technology and people (Fig. 6.8). Innovation is therefore managed as an integrated technical and organisational system. Strategies and objectives are worked through to detailed plans and actions. At all times attention is given to where we are now and where we want to be along a wide range of dimensions. This then gives us the gap analysis against which we can define our plans, commit our resources and monitor our progress.

In conclusion, the project team has to manage change through both direct and indirect means. The team requires the resources, the skills, the power and the influence to ensure that both direct and indirect means are managed as an integrated whole.

Summary

The direct means of managing technological change are those which are the most measurable and tangible. Organisation and planning systems provide the prerequisites for technological change, but they are insufficient on their own. Even so, there are many ways in which we can improve our 'direct' systems to ensure greater clarity and effectiveness.

The indirect means of managing innovation

The indirect means are not optional. Soft they may be, but nevertheless they are crucial to success. In a recent survey of senior managers in the USA the managers gave their views on managing innovation (Tables 6.1–6.3).

Most of the issues raised concerning the factors which encourage and discourage innovation are not issues about what we have called the 'direct'

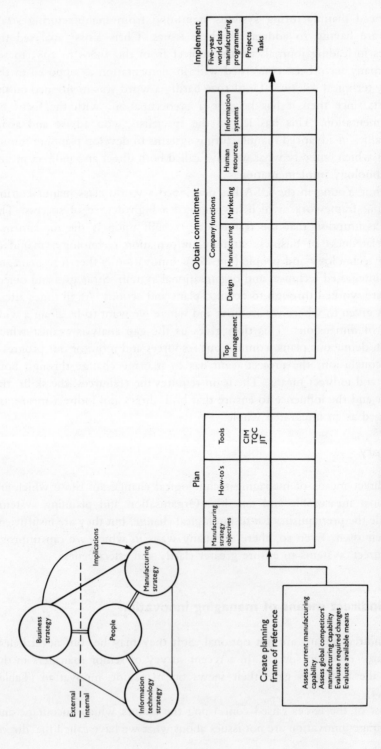

Fig. 6.8 An integrated manufacturing implementation framework. *Source:* Gunn T. G. (1987) *Manufacturing for Competitive Advantage*

Table 6.1 Factors which encourage innovation

Based on your experience, what two recommendations would you give to companies that wish to significantly increase their rates of successful innovation?

Recommendations	Percentage of respondents citing this factor
1. Increase or improve market research efforts or capacity	29.8%
2. Get top management commitment and support or leadership	17.0%
3. Increase rewards or establish a reward system for innovative groups and individuals	17.0%
4. Encourage risk taking and avoid penalising mistakes	15.6%
5. Improve or establish a positive, more entrepreneurial climate for innovation	12.5%
6. Increase creative, entrepreneurial, far-sighted thinking and behaviour	8.1%
7. Establish separate or small organisational units responsible for innovative activities	5.7%
8. Establish clear priorities, goals, objectives	5.7%
9. Delegate authority and responsibility: decentralisation	5.7%
10. Develop differentiation in products or services	5.3%
11. Use innovative strategies or formulate an innovation plan	5.1%
12. Persist in innovation efforts	5.1%

Source: Young, A. (1985) *Innovation: The Agenda for American Business.*

means of managing change. The concerns are about the organisation, its values and its ability to support and give resources to its potential innovators. Even when we look at the reasons stated for new product or service failure (Table 6.4), these other or 'indirect' features are seen as important, albeit behind the issues of market and competitor analysis.

Table 6.2 Factors which discourage innovation

What single factor most discourages innovation in your company?

Inhibiting factor	Percentage of respondents citing this factor
1. Fear of failure or risk taking	14.8%
2. Red tape/cumbersome decision and review structure or process	10.1%
3. Lack of funds for innovation	9.9%
4. Preoccupation with current operations at the expense of future opportunities	8.7%
5. Failure to engage in innovative thinking/insistence on tradition	6.9%
6. Lack of top management support, commitment, or innovativeness	6.1%
7. Organisational structure that discourages innovation	5.1%

Source: Young, A. (1985) *Innovation: The Agenda for American Business.*

Table 6.3   Barriers to innovation

There are many barriers to innovation. Please check the three most important barriers to innovation within your company.

Barriers	Percentage of respondents citing this barrier
1. Cannot afford; inadequate return on investment	44.9%
2. Tendency to protect an existing investment or livelihood	43.7%
3. Fear of failure	31.8%
4. The 'not-invented-here' syndrome	28.1%
5. 'Let's postpone it; give it some more thought'	27.9%
6. Opposes custom, habit, fashion, taste	26.9%
7. 'That product won't work' or 'It didn't work last time'	18.2%
8. We are basically followers, not leaders	16.8%

Source: Young, A. (1985) *Innovation: The Agenda for American Business.*

Table 6.4   Reasons for new product or service failure

There are many reasons for new product or new service failure. Of the twelve selected below, check the three most important reasons for failure in your industry.

Reasons for new product and service failure	Percentage of respondents citing this reason
Insufficient or faulty market/customer needs analysis	61.1%
Lack of proper competitive assessment	38.1%
Too much of a 'me-too'	27.1%
Strayed from corporate or marketing expertise	23.7%
Developed or marketed too slow or too fast	22.5%
Lack of top management involvement/commitment	22.3%

Source: Young, A. (1985) *Innovation: The Agenda for American Business.*

Top management commitment

A commitment to technological innovation at the highest level in the organisation is imperative. To be sure, we have developed ideas of 'bottom-up' as well as 'top-down' innovation, indicating in some cases that innovation occurs despite the organisation. Such guerrilla activity can be quite effective, but only on a small scale. If the organisation suppresses innovation the big leaps will never occur.

Too often members of boards will say, 'We are committed. The R&D manager is on the board. Surely that is enough?'. No, it is not enough.

In one company 'new technology' was given to the engineering director. Funds were allocated and he was given the task of getting on with it. It was deemed to be a functional, segmented activity to be delegated or dumped down the line. The fact that the technology in question fundamentally challenged work practices, service standards and costs in each of the other divisions of the company went unnoticed until the equipment was installed. The resistance then came to the fore with a vengeance as the other directors fought to maintain their existing systems.

There are a number of specific actions and indicators of top management commitment:

- How many technologists are there on the board?
- Is technology part of the business planning process?
- Do board members visibly champion projects or do they adopt a 'wait and see whether it works' attitude?
- Does the board communicate a vision of the future?
- Is the board open to being lobbied by people with ideas?
- How does the board deal with failure?

In any project that involves risk the final approval of the board to proceed is very rarely a licence for the project champion and his or her team to go away and get on with their work free from interruptions, investigations and further questions about the project's survival.

Example

In 1837, the inspector of the British Navy, Sir William Symonds, expressed the following opinion of the usefulness of ship screws: '... even if the screw had the force to propel the ship, this would be completely useless, because the ship could not be steered due to the screw's effect at the stern of the vessel.'

In 1839, the well-known surgeon, Alfred Velpeau, wrote about anaesthesia: 'The elimination of pain in surgery is a wild notion. Aspiring to it is absurd at the present time. In surgery "knife" and "pain" are two words that will forever have to remain connected with one another in the patient's mind.'

Such people still exist in every organisation. They are not likely to be wreckers; they are probably highly dedicated, conscientious people with a great love of the world as it now is. Senior management need to have the vision and the courage of their convictions, and must ensure that they keep close to their project teams, because what is certain is that they will be heavily lobbied by those who believe that the project is too risky or too threatening, and who do not actually understand it anyway.

It is therefore essential for project teams to have highly tuned political and lobbying skills in order to keep top managers informed of progress, discuss the good and the bad, and give feedback which will reinforce the total vision. There are few organisations where there are not a number of 'experts' who will have a different view of technological progress.

Top management need to be visible to the whole organisation in their commitment to technological change. Too often we see our role as primarily controlling rather than leading; vetoing and censoring rather than enthusing and promoting.

Innovation requires the innovators to gain commitment from the top and continue to convince them that the project is right. That commitment must be spread to all those who are affected by the project and all those who can frustrate, disrupt and sabotage their efforts. It is an interesting exercise to sit down with your board to analyse areas where commitment is weak and discuss the advantages to individuals of staying as they are.

Actively managing the culture

Culture can be changed only with great effort, persistence and clear focus. Our corporations are littered with a plethora of initiatives which are *ad hoc*, contradictory and poorly sponsored. Focus of purpose, staying power and clarity of direction are key. If we decide that our communications need improvement, then we should look at them in the integrated way depicted in Fig. 6.9, where each aspect of the way a business communicates can be seen to reinforce and develop a single set of values.

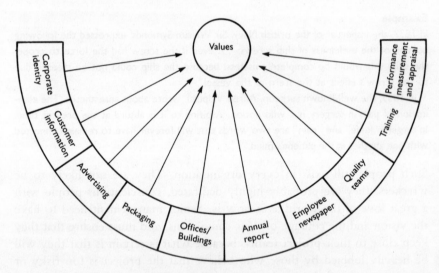

Fig. 6.9 An integrated communications strategy

If we want to give a consistent message to our employees it must be the same message that we are giving our customers. Telling the customer about the value we place on quality will soon be shown to be a sham unless the same message is well communicated internally. That then links with our corporate identity, our packaging, our offices and all manifestations of our corporate culture. Different messages create confusion and reduce credibility, which the customer will be the first to pick up.

Corporate culture

This may be defined as the body of norms, conceptions of value and attitudes which affect the actions of employees at all levels and thereby influence the characteristics of an organisation.

We shall change our culture when we change and live by our values. The answers to the following questions tell us much about the values which are behind what we actually practise:

- Is it more important to please my boss or the customer?
- Can I really afford to make a mistake?
- Do I believe that if the system says, therefore I must do?
- Do I push for volume when I know the specification is not correct?
- Do I take responsibility for problems rather than blaming others?

We may conclude that our culture does wholly support our business strategy. Even where it does, this is no reason for complacency; we still need deliberately to maintain and cultivate that culture with energy and enthusiasm. If, as is more likely, there are discrepancies or indeed if we find that the organisation has very little of a recognisable culture, then we need plans and actions to achieve the culture which can deliver our business strategy. In Chapter 8 we show in more detail how we can audit the culture of an organisation.

The emphasis we place on the direct means of managing innovation will demonstrate the value we place on efficiency as opposed to excellence, the immediate as opposed to the important, the consistent as opposed to the productive. These will be effective only if they are reinforced and institutionalised through the indirect means (Fig. 6.10).

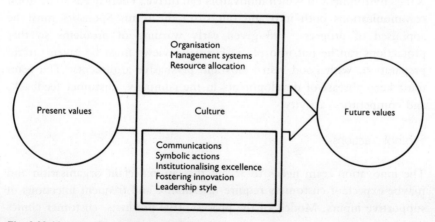

Fig. 6.10 Managing the corporate culture

The role of the top management team in changing the corporate culture is to:

- translate the new values into their own behaviour (i.e. the top managers much change first);
- communicate the new values to every level of the organisation;
- provide training to support the new behaviour;
- shift power towards people whose skills, values and behaviour support the new culture;
- identify where possible high-impact systems and use them to steer people's behaviour;
- reward the desired behaviour;
- be patient and allow enough time for the new culture to take hold.

There are some pretty tough decisions to be made in this list, often requiring new people in the key top posts in order to show that a real change is to be made.

There are two aspects of culture management: the influence of the innovation team and the project manager in particular, and that of the broader organisation, the project sponsors in particular. Both aspects are equally important.

The innovation team: the project manager's influence

Communications

The team needs ways of communicating constantly with all members. There must be room for them on their own to brainstorm, drink coffee, swap experiences, support each other, and get to know each other. This is the environment in which innovators can thrive. There needs to be good communications both into and out from the team. Sponsors must be appraised of progress, and given early warning of problems so that protections can be put into place. Formal reviews must be given careful preparation, with good visual aids and persuasive arguments. The team must keep abreast of developments in the company, customer feedback, and competitors' activity.

Symbolic actions

The innovation team needs to accept that an expectant organisation and maybe expectant customers require reassurance and frequent injections of supportive inputs. Models of the process, trial products, customer clinics and employee demonstrations provide the reassurance that the money is being well spent. It was only after the symbolic gesture of giving away the post-it notes in the sales and marketing departments of 3M that they were convinced of the potential market: a creative piece of marketing by an innovation team!

Institutionalising excellence

The innovation team needs to ensure that it works to the highest standards, and nothing else will do. Actions include selecting the best people, regularly monitoring their performance, ensuring that attention is given to detail and the follow-through (many an innovation has lost out not in concept but in detail), and ensuring that there is a pervasive application of effort which comes from the deepest commitment to the new process, product or technology. Institutionalising excellence embraces how the team is structured and where it is positioned in the wider organisation, the decision support systems that it employs, the values it demonstrates, and its day-to-day practices.

Fostering innovation

The project leader or champion has to negotiate sufficient space to develop an open and participative approach which will discuss failure as well as success, setbacks as well as progress, and which will treat team members as valued colleagues rather than technical subordinates. Teamwork and group problem-solving skills will be high, and specific time will be put aside to allow for new ideas to be discussed. The pressure for completion often leads to tunnel vision, with the obvious being missed and the genius being forgotten. The team needs a positive enjoyment of argument and each member should be sufficiently confident to be prepared to be uncomfortable and have his or her ideas challenged, analysed and sometimes rejected.

Leadership style

Much will depend upon the management skills and leadership style of the project champion. The strongest messages will not come from what the project manager says, but from what he or she does. How does the leader spend his or her time? What actually gets rewarded in the team and what behaviour gets punished? Who gets promoted and where is the money spent?

Culture in the company

In the company the innovation team needs the space and the support to operate effectively. The ground must also be prepared so that new technologies are welcomed rather than treated with fear and hostility by the affected groups in the organisation.

Example

The UK arm of a large US defence electronics company has its R&D and engineering development group on the same site as the production and servicing teams. There was a constant battle between the two. The production and servicing teams were asking why it was that the researchers were allowed to come in late when the production operators were being quartered for being more than two minutes late. There was a feeling that 'they never do any work, sitting around chatting all day'. From the development teams came constant complaints of being railroaded down production-orientated systems and procedures which were quite inappropriate for intelligent engineers. Neither understood each other, their values were different and little was being done to gain understanding and cooperation between the two, which is essential for effective product development.

Communications

This is essential to constantly reinforce the fact that this company actively seeks and welcomes change. There are a wide range of potential 'delivery vehicles' and much will depend on the type of organisation, the message, the type of people, and so on. The key is the focus and direction of those communications: progress on key projects, what the competition is doing, examples of successful individual and group change, and developing the vision of the future.

Communications is a two-way process; it is not just a question of keeping people informed of progress. Within the culture which we are trying to create is the expectation and desire for everyone to *respond* rather than absorb. This is time-consuming and requires a conscious effort: effort to listen to all ideas and opinions and to try as far as possible to build on them. In Chapter 5 we noted that in Japan not only is the incidence of staff suggestions much higher than in Europe and the United States, but also a much larger proportion of suggestions are adopted by companies. This can only be a product of good, open listening and the building of ideas one on another.

Symbolic actions

It will rarely make a direct material difference to a project for the chairperson to take a direct interest in an innovation's success, but in terms of visible support, sending messages of value, it is symbolically vital. Those in every organisation who work assiduously to ensure the project's failure will be warned off; it will be just that much harder for the finance director to propose trimming back the expenditure. If the chairperson or chief executive is known for only one thing it should be for supporting innovation. Other symbolic actions are to ensure that all those who will be affected in any way by the impact of the technology feel some ownership of it. Models, demonstrations and simulators all reduce fear and enable people to relate to and buy into the future.

Example
During the planning stage of an advanced manufacturing line the company set aside a room with a programmable robot arm, self-learning programmes and models and outline plans for the new facility. Slowly people became interested; the place became packed during break times and at the end of the shift. More units had to be ordered. The complaint soon came from the operators that management was dragging its heels in implementing the new line.

Institutionalising excellence

In the wider organisation there are four components. Two of these are tangible and recognisable; the other two can be seen only in the way we act and behave at work.

The tangible components are the visible part of the iceberg (Fig. 6.11) and comprise the organisation's structure and support systems. 'Excellence' here means focusing on the primary purpose of the organisation and its customers and on ensuring that there are mechanisms in place to keep everyone in touch with the customers' needs, their own and the corporate performance, and resource utilisation. Each structure and system is seen to reinforce the customer focus and add value at each stage.

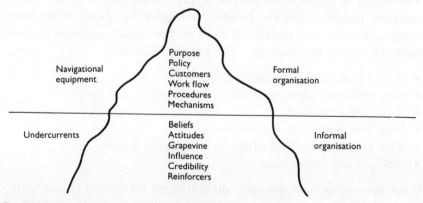

Fig. 6.11 Institutionalising excellence: the iceberg

Below the water level are our actual values and practices. Too often we have a gap between these and our formal organisation and business proclamations. It means that what we believe and practise is inconsistent with what we say. Sitting on the fence is not possible; if you are not part of the solution, then you are part of the problem.

For example, having a common language, ensuring that everyone knows what is expected of them, understanding both internal and external customer demands, and ensuring the delivery of quality are all ways in which organisations seek to institutionalise excellence.

Fostering innovation

The innovative company is innovative throughout; innovation is not confined to project teams or R&D. Incremental improvement in all jobs all the time is the predominant value. This may be achieved through quality or improvement circles. It is, however, the openness of our management, our spirit of play and our determination to be leaders in our market which may be more effective. Systems subservience and excessive segmentation in the organisation have to be removed. The guardians of those systems will prophesy doom, and their power and influence may have to be diluted.

Leadership style

The behaviour of the most visible and influential people in the organisation is the largest single influence on its culture. Where it is known that the directors constantly squabble, guard their domains, undermine board decisions and cover their backs there is little point in asking R&D to improve innovation and the personnel department to change the culture. The money is better spent on the works outing! Whatever the glossy company magazine *says* the business strategy is all about, of far more influence is what they actually do about it. The grapevine should give the same message as the magazine. The key questions are:

- How do the leaders spend their time?
- Does this have anything to do with technology and innovation?
- What gets rewarded?
- What gets punished?
- Who gets promoted? (And do they champion innovation?)
- Where is the money spent?

If the answers to these questions do not match the desired culture of the company (and that is the one which will deliver the business strategy), then we will condemn ourselves to yet more well-meaning but ineffective initiatives which will cost us money and deliver confusion.

Learning from experience

The management of innovation is an uncertain process to which we hope we have given some illumination and guidance. A depressing feature of many of the organisations we have studied is that they appear to learn from neither success nor failure; the management of innovation is not seen as a management priority. There is much we can learn from both our own and others' success and failure.

Example
ICI paints have developed a clear and understood approach to the management of new technology. It is not perfect, but is constantly being built upon and improved. Project champions have a broad brief to develop and implement technological change. The project managers are trained in technical and managerial areas. Organisational interfaces between the project and the user are managed, and their success rate looks pretty impressive.

Summary

How we manage technological change is as important as the technology we wish to introduce. We need deliberate strategies for managing technology and we have choices to make about which strategy is appropriate in the individual circumstances.

The way we relate to and assist teams set up to manage change is as important as the internal management of those teams.

Success comes from the conscious management of what we have described as the indirect as well as the more familiar direct means of managing change.

References

1. Diebold, J. & Associates (1982) *The Survey of Implementation Issues.*
2. Little Arthur D. (1985) *Management Perspectives on Innovation.*
3. Nadler, G. and Robinson, G. (1987) Planning, designing and implementing

advanced manufacturing technology. In Wall, T. (ed.) *The Human Side of Advanced Manufacturing Technology*, Wiley.

4. Voss, C. (1986) Implementing manufacturing technology: a manufacturing approach. In Twiss, B. (ed.) *Operations Management in the 1990s*. MCB.

5. Gunn, T. G. (1987) *Manufacturing for Competitive Advantage*. Ballinger.

7 Developing managers for technological change

In an entrepreneurial society, both individuals and institutions develop habits of flexibility, of continuous learning, and of acceptance of change as normal and as opportunity.

Peter F. Drucker, 1985

We have so far considered a wide range of factors in the organisation which influence the way in which we embrace and exploit technology. We have put forward techniques, examples of successful innovation and some of the pitfalls on the way. The bottom line, however, is the extent to which we can influence and actively change organisational and, in particular, individual behaviour to improve business performance through technology.

This chapter addresses some of the ways in which highly successful companies have influenced people at all organisational levels: influenced and changed them, made better use of their skills, removed some of the blockages, and brought the management of technological change into the forefront of management activity rather than being an *ad hoc* afterthought. At one level the chapter is about training; at another it is about a powerful tool which helps organisations to change. What is quite certain is that unless we improve and develop the way we manage, we are most unlikely to achieve a competitive edge over our competitors, particularly those which are proving successful in translating new technology into high-demand products.

There are few, if any, prescriptions for the development of managers. We shall examine some examples from the UK, Japan and the USA and hope by so doing to demonstrate the diversity of success in ensuring that our managers in particular, and our entire workforces in general, can manage and embrace, rather than resist, technologically stimulated change.

We shall consider three target groups: top management, the innovation project team, and the wider organisation. Inevitably there is overlap between the development needs of these three groups, a point which serves to emphasise the need for a unified approach to developing the innovative organisation. The chapter concludes with a 'toolkit' of techniques and approaches commonly used in the innovative organisation which can be learned and exploited.

Developing innovative top managers

Technologies, systems and bright ideas are of little value if top management teams do not have two key characteristics:

- strategic thinking and direction;
- an active approach to culture building to implement the strategy.

Business strategy as an idea and certainly as a technique used in boardrooms has become increasingly popular over the past five years. The idea of a strategy defining a long-range plan has become diluted and dissipated as businesses have seen one five-year forecast after another cast into the bin because the future really is not that predictable. The interest in strategy has more to do with concentration of effort, resources, and the increasing understanding that corporate survival is to do with innovation, renewal and change.

So often the simplistic notion that a company is in business to secure profit and nothing else has led to investment in anything which is likely to yield the predetermined rate of return. The direction of the company becomes confused and energy is dissipated as different markets and cultures struggle and compete with one another within the same corporation. The less than 50 per cent success rate of acquisitions[1] seems to support this conclusion.

Strategy is the setting of organisational direction, providing the focus for the organisation's resources, the vision, logic and framework within which all members of the organisation can dedicate their efforts. In terms of Tom Peters' ship, it is the bottom of the hull, that which is the logic for the organisation's existence. In a rapidly changing world everything else in the organisation has to be open to challenge and change, but there still has to be some superordinate purpose which is the reason for its very existence.

The aim of strategy is to achieve a pre-eminent management technique which results in higher quality performance and superior management of change than competitive organisations.

Business strategy is not only the positioning (current and future) of the organisation in the marketplace; it has to embrace how technology, people and the organisation are going to be focused to achieve that strategy.

The development of senior management to consider and embrace a business strategy which sees technology as an active strategic component appears to be rarely practised in the UK.[2] Instead the most common options are either to get consultants to determine your strategy for you or to send some of the key directors to a strategy programme at a leading business school.

The disadvantage of the former is that externally imposed solutions are rarely sufficiently well accepted, believed in or implemented to achieve radical change. As for the latter, our experience and research have shown that, in these programmes, technology is very rarely seen as a strategic component and that implementation, particularly in terms of what we have called culture, is weak or missing altogether. The competitive alliance between business strategy, technology and culture development is missed.

Too often the gesture of sending a director to learn about strategy means that it is then seen to be his or her problem. The collective responsibility of the board for strategy is projected onto one person or a small group of individuals.

There is starting to emerge a third solution: using strategy development as a process of top management development to achieve not only an effective strategy, but the leadership, the determination, and the concentration of effort required to manage complex organisational change.

One such approach has been developed by Arthur Young consultants.[3] In this approach, based on a series of top team workshops, the board is taken through a process of team building, strategy generation and planning for its implementation. Through the workshop environment a common language is established within which differences in idea and approach can be examined and resolved.

The workshops are necessarily served with data (analyses of and technical information on the organisation, products, markets and environ-

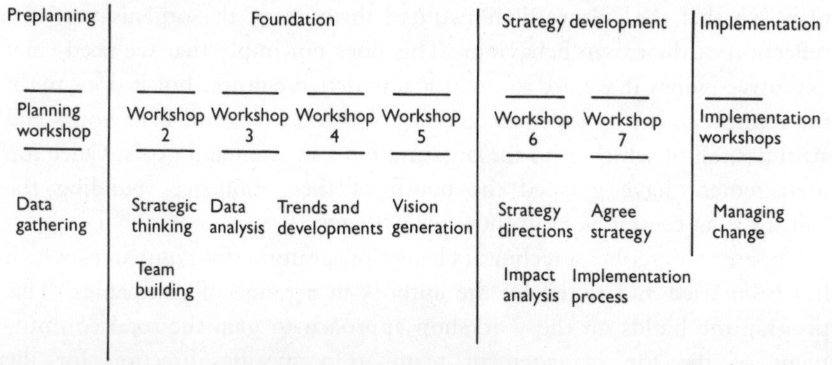

Preplanning	Foundation				Strategy development		Implementation
Planning workshop	Workshop 2	Workshop 3	Workshop 4	Workshop 5	Workshop 6	Workshop 7	Implementation workshops
Data gathering	Strategic thinking	Data analysis	Trends and developments	Vision generation	Strategy directions	Agree strategy	Managing change
	Team building				Impact analysis	Implementation process	

Fig. 7.1 A workshop framework for strategy development

ment) and therefore are able to use the process as both a problem-solving and a decision-making exercise. Deriving strategy in this manner starts of itself the first steps of culture development. It ensures that the top team are committed to the interrelatedness of innovation and culture. The whole process can then be rolled down the organisation as a focused and well thought-through direction for the company (Fig. 7.1).

Part of developing strategy in this way is the generation of the familiar mission, values and goals statements. Apart from being extremely difficult to agree upon, why do we do it? The mission, values and goals statements we believe are of particular value in the management of innovation.

Clarity of purpose in an organisation is of the utmost importance if we are to weld a cohesive and purposeful group of people. The problem is that, with accelerating change, it can become particularly difficult for those in the middle and lower levels of the organisation to sense that direction. In the bureaucratic and segmented organisation the ostensible purpose is quite clear, but as we learn to thrive on chaos in a fluid and dynamic organisation it can become quite confusing. Therefore clarity of direction is *more important* to the innovative organisation.

An active approach to building the culture which will implement the strategy has to be combined with the development of the strategy itself. In Chapters 2 and 6 we examined the elements to culture which support strategy. The top team need more than just awareness of this; they need to be able to change their own behaviour if the culture is to change appreciably. Part of this awareness is of the strengths and weaknesses of the top team itself. Who are the natural farmers, fishermen and train drivers? Top teams also need to be aware of whether they have the elements of an effective team. One method for looking at this is outlined below under team building.

Top management, to all intents and purposes, are the representatives of the organisation's culture. Like it or not, they are on show, the exemplars, so that the culture demonstrated throughout the organisation is a reflection of their own behaviour. This does not imply that we need chief executive clones if we are to build a supportive culture, but it does mean the reinforcement by top management of a wide range of behaviours and attitudes, all of which echo the organisation's mission and goals. Once top management have grasped the depth of their influence, building the culture is as central as how they behave every day.

Chapter 8 describes a technical change programme for companies which has been tried and tested by the authors in a range of companies. This programme builds on the workshop approach to gain the total commitment of the top management team to a specific direction for the organisation.

Summary

- Strategic thinking can be developed in top teams.
- Strategy is the collective responsibility of the board and must be championed by each member.
- The most effective approach combines team building with the development of the long-term vision.
- Top teams need to be more aware of the extent to which they promote, retard or just block innovation.

Developing the innovative project team

The innovative project team will in all likelihood be put together from a range of sections and departments. The resulting structure can therefore assume a complex matrix form. Peters and Waterman[4] exhort us to keep things simple, which may suffice for incremental technological change, but for highly complex technologies requiring the integration of a wide range of technical as well as business expertise there are no simple forms of organisation. In the USA[5] a study of electronics companies has found that it can take between two and three years before managers start to feel the benefits of a matrix project organisation. Those who have just one boss will at first have difficulty in working in project teams with at least two sets of different reporting relationships: relating to the project manager for resources, planning and progress and relating to the functional boss on technical expertise.

In this complex web, training and development can greatly improve the effectiveness of the team. The paradox facing many managers is that advancing science and technology requires ever more specialist knowledge and understanding if true competitive advantage is to be found. This depth of expertise, however, is of little value if it is not accompanied by a broad understanding of how the expertise might be applied to a business. Much emphasis in this book is placed upon the need to have technology champions, but we also need people who can bridge the gap between technology development and a successful product. We have from this paradox two sets of needs: the capture and development of potentially useful technology and the appreciation of broad business needs.

We can therefore conceive of the T-shaped technologist and the T-shaped business manager (Fig. 7.2). For the technologist the leg of the T is his or her depth of expertise in his or her particular field. The top bar is a broad appreciation of business direction and market understanding. For the business manager, the leg of the T is his or her depth of expertise

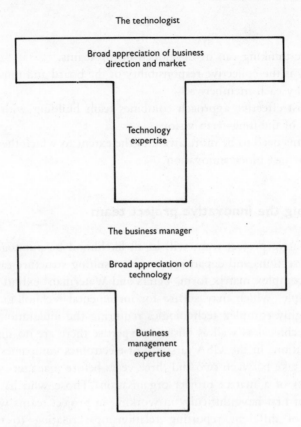

Fig. 7.2 The T-shaped manager and technologist

in business management and the bar is an appreciation of how technology can be used for competitive advantage.

In a recent study of management training initiatives in the United Kingdom which support technology management it is quite evident that very few management training establishments include these cross-functional perspectives when they train either technologists or business managers. They can be brought together by senior managers who will institute advice, cross-functional secondments and experimentation with new and different technologies and integrated business education.

The project team, on formation, will be put under pressure to perform. Its composition, how well it functions, and how it communicates are fundamental to its success.

Project management skills

The evaluation of UK government-sponsored innovation projects[6] has highlighted project management skills and expertise as a major weakness in implementing technically sound solutions.

A thorough understanding of the desired form of project management is crucial if the project is to survive in the broader organisation. Where this is not established we have found great value in developing this framework with both the team and its 'clients' within the organisation. Project management needs to combine the content, roles, responsibilities and measures of performance with the process issues of *how* these are to be carried out.

Example

A precision instruments company appointed a project manager to introduce a new product into their factory. The new product required a step change in process technology. After six months there was little visible progress. The man had beavered away conscientiously but had no resources to enable him to achieve his task. The resource providers saw the manager's role as planning, not doing; the latter was their responsibility. The problem was that neither the project manager nor the resource providers had accepted responsibility for jointly working out their respective and complementary roles.

The project team itself may extend beyond the immediate organisation. People from research labs, customers and universities may all be involved, thereby testing our project manager's skills to the utmost. The implementation of technological change will also involve the project team with a great number of contractors and subcontractors, the management of which would need to be the subject of a separate book.

Team building

A team is only a team by virtue of sharing responsibility for a specified output. Whilst these core members are responsible for the outcome, others may be co-opted onto the team to provide specialist information, advice and expertise.

Effective teams are made up of different types of people. People who have worked in research, engineering and R&D departments for long periods may be particularly strong as technical specialists, but less strong or undeveloped in the other components of an effective team. Many organisations have built and developed teams using Belbin's team typing. Innovative teams will need a chairperson, a strength in finishing and following through, shapers and team builders along with the more familiar technical skills of the resource investigator, the monitor/evaluator and the ideas person (Table 7.1).

Table 7.1   The constituent elements of an effective team (Belbin)

Function	Qualities
Chair	Calm, self-confident, keeps the team focused on its objectives, ensures best use of its members
Shaper	Outgoing, dynamic, shapes the application of group effort, challenges inertia
Company worker	Systematic, hard-working, turns the plans into workable actions, organises people and events
Ideas person	Unorthodox, individualistic, imaginative, looks for new ideas and approaches
Resource investigator	Enthusiastic, curious, creates external contacts, conducts useful negotiations
Monitor/evaluator	Hard-headed, prudent, analyses problems and evaluates ideas for the team's benefit
Team builder	Socially oriented, supportive of the team, fosters team spirit and growth
Completer/finisher	Conscientious, orderly, follows through on decisions, maintains a sense of urgency
Specialist	Expert, provider of know-how, meticulous searcher for data, curious, intellectual, opinion valued, may often be used to research ideas and opinions

Reproduced with kind permission from R. M. Belbin, *Management Teams* Heinemann.

Communications

The project team needs to communicate with its primary sponsors, the organisation at large, the marketplace, and sources of expertise and materials. Therefore project teams need to be effective presenters and communicators. Often a regular project briefing sheet keeping everyone up to date can maintain interest, enthusiasm and commitment to the project. Formal presentation skills are required for the board, customers and financial institutions if additional capital is being raised to fund the project. The 'In Search of Excellence' video[7] has an excellent sequence showing the interrogations a project manager is likely to experience in 3M – compulsory viewing for all project champions.

Briefing skills are often required when a team member explains to a group of operators what the technology is all about and how it will affect them and their jobs.

Finally, a project team which is not only tough but also charming gets much further than one which is abrasive and protective. The team must exude an air of confidence and optimisim. If any member starts to show doubts it will spread like wildfire and trigger opposition.

Developing the innovative organisation

Responsibility for developing the innovative organisation lies primarily with management. Their skills, attitudes and vision are key to building the organisational commitment to and competence in an innovative environment. In one of the lesser known books on excellence[8] there are listed the six conventional, fundamental skills of good management practice as exercised by most of our business schools. These are summarised as:

- Set goals and establish policies and procedures.
- Organise, motivate and control people.
- Analyse situations and formulate strategic operating plans.
- Respond to change through new strategies and reorganisations.
- Implement change by issuing new policies and procedures.
- Get results and produce respectable growth, profitability and return on investment.

These are no longer sufficient. They may achieve the maintenance of stable organisations but are insufficient to capture innovation and change. Their 'new age skills' they summarise as:

- creative insight;
- sensitivity;
- vision;
- versatility;
- focus;
- patience.

The difference between these two sets of skills is largely between the maintenance management tasks and the developmental management tasks. As we have seen, these two sets of skills must often lie uncomfortably beside each other, and the innovative company manages the interface between the two. The difference is captured by the functions of the two sides of the brain: we have concentrated most management development on the left; we now need to develop more of the right-hand side. Some of the techniques which can be used to improve our 'right side of brain' are included in our kitbag of tools and techniques (see later).

There are five routes by which the company managers can stimulate development of an innovative culture. These are discussed below.

The implications of technological change

Managers responsible for and involved in technological change need lateral vision. They need to understand the impact of changed products and processes on the many issues that we examined in Chapter 4, and their implications. Much of the information about this impact will come from those affected by the change, and overall recognition is required that this is as important as, if not more important than, the effective technology itself, because it is here that the greatest barriers to change occur.

In the same way that the overall business strategy must be allied with the right culture for its implementation, so must the technologist and the business manager be concerned with the culture into which the technology is to be placed and how it can provide the growing medium for successful exploitation.

The are a few good case studies which can help teams address some of these issues. One of the simplest and most effective is one which the authors have used in their workshop programmes.

Example. Ugg and Bogg: a case study in the implications of technological change
Ugg and Bogg have operated successfully for many years as carriers. Between them they have carried all the cave's water supplies, dragged in the dinosaur carcasses and collected roots and berries. Because of their strength and expertise they are the official bearers of King Og to the daily place of worship. As a result of this the cave is dependent upon them and they are accorded privileges (extra pterodactyl and a place near the fire).

One day, as Ugg and Bogg are carrying water, Ack bursts through the bushes in great excitement. He is carrying a smooth, slim log with a circular, flat cross-section of tree trunk attached to each end.

Discuss the implications for Ugg and Bogg.

Such case studies are of great use in getting groups to consider the technical, work organisation, power, control and organisational issues.

Processes of technological change

In Chapter 6 we looked at a range of strategies and processes for managing technological change. The understanding of these and the associated skills for their execution are largely ignored by general management and technologists alike. Systems planning is the easy part. The difficult part is gaining first of all the understanding and acceptance that the process of change is worth attending to and that there is a set of skills which are needed to properly effect change.

There are relatively few good programmes on change management and even fewer which integrate ideas of change alongside changed technology. It is often left up to the company itself to work with insiders or outsiders to develop practical and relevant programmes for innovators. Our studies in Japan demonstrated that a considerable amount of effort is put into change management programmes for R&D as well as operations staff. The mandatory system of management training in Japan may seem rigid, but it does ensure a common level of understanding and a common language within which they manage their projects.

Technology awareness

During our study tour in Japan we were fascinated by the thriving technical seminar business. These are companies which arrange and organise a wide range of technical seminars, usually of one day's duration, which appear to act as an interchange and dissemination process for leading-edge ideas. Two features are remarkable: the popularity of the seminars and the nature of the participants. Access to these seminars was quite open in many of the companies we visited. They were open to and attended by both specialists and non-specialists in the subject area of the seminar. Metal companies will freely send people on biotechnology seminars, personnel specialists will attend those on microelectronics. It was claimed that such seminars play an important role in technology transfer. The speakers are usually drawn from universities, or companies whose competitors will freely attend.

The seminar industry is also connected with a range of technical correspondence courses which are often taken up voluntarily by employees to ensure that they have the necessary knowledge and skills for the future.

Such apparent open access to technological understanding within companies is refreshing, against our often specialist/functionalist approach in the West. Even if we are sceptical about its effectiveness at keeping leading-edge technologists fully up to date in their subject area, it is certainly of immense value to the non-specialist who is striving to build the technology transfer bridges.

As the overall levels of training in the UK demonstrate, insufficient priority and resources are put into training. This tends to ensure that the training which is done is of a highly technical and specialist nature, leading towards professional rather than business qualifications.

Staff attitudes: from control to commitment

We have already talked about the powerful influence that both managers and the project team have on attitude within the organisation. However, building competence and commitment, and therefore a positive attitude to change, requires as much attention as that given to the technology.

Within our companies in their entirety there is the need for sometimes quite radical changes in attitude. In a manufacturing example, we can see the required shift to be that shown in Table 7.2.

Table 7.2 Required attitude changes

From	To
Little boxes	The big picture
Complacency	Competitiveness
Manufacturing is a cost centre	Manufacturing capability is a strategic source of competitive advantage
Top management is a roadblock	Top management *leads the way*
Inventory is an asset	Inventory is a liability
It's not my job	It's everyone's job
Serial vertical communication	Open horizontal and vertical communication
Just hit the goal; save some for the next time	Improve day by day
I'm not allowed to	I am encouraged to
Not invented here	Use it if it works; learn from others
Do it ourselves	Buy it
Planning is no good and not needed here	Planning is beneficial; we must plan
Number games	Truth, accurate data and information: no 'filters'
We know what's best for the customer	The customer is always right
Computers are a cost	Computers are a competitive asset
Data control and definition are unimportant.	Data is a corporate resource, to be defined and controlled effectively

Source: Gunn, T. G. (1987) *Manufacturing for Competitive Advantage*. Ballinger.

Gunn[9] says, '. . . time and time again, the major impediment to the implementation of world class manufacturing is people: their lack of knowledge, their resistance to change, or simply their lack of ability to quickly absorb the vast multitude of new technologies, philosophies, ideas, practices that have come about in manufacturing over the last five to ten years. *Only education and training can solve this problem.*'

The sheer volume of training which is required to successfully implement change is often grossly underestimated. The training has to have the dual purpose of building both *competence* and *commitment* side by side.

Example

Norsk Hydro is a large Norwegian company with extensive fertiliser interests in the UK. Changes in agricultural policies have increased competition as the overall demand has dropped. Faced with the choice of rundown or investment, they chose the latter, investing heavily in a new, highly efficient process plant. Radical changes in working practices were introduced, including a single-union agreement and high levels of flexibility. To support these initiatives the pay system was changed to reward individuals for new skill acquisition within an annual working pattern which allows eleven days' training per employee each year.

It is only through the commitment of time and resources such as has been demonstrated in companies like Norsk Hydro and British Steel that competence levels will rise so that new technologies and skills are welcomed rather than feared and resisted.

The learning company

Norsk Hydro, British Steel and similar companies which have achieved major change are moving towards becoming learning companies. The concept is the creation of the environment and opportunity within the company for each and every individual to grow through learning. The opportunities will span from open and distance learning to job rotation and experiential learning. The costs are borne partly by the individual and partly by the company.

Development in the company is shifted from a 'pull' model (We need more fitters; who can we train?) to more of a 'push' model. In the 'push' model we encourage people to develop themselves so that when we have a vacancy we have a pool of qualified people from whom to choose. The concept may seem wasteful inasmuch as one runs the risk of over-training people and losing them to other employers. It may also appear to be excessively expensive to train more people than one actually needs at any one moment in time. If trained labour is plentiful then this argument becomes quite powerful. If, however, it is not, it is no use waiting until the FMS (Flexible Manufacturing System) line is ordered to start to consider the training aspects. As several major companies have found, it is just too late and they have had to rely on highly expensive external resources.

The innovative company's kitbag of skills and techniques

The skills and techniques used for management in an organisation are wide and varied. There are few commonly understood competencies and often we find the same idea implanted under a variety of labels. In generating this kitbag we do not attempt to be exhaustive; rather we attempt to emphasise those approaches we believe support an innovative culture. Further details of these techniques can be found in the references for this chapter.

Typically the innovative company will use a set of techniques to:

- demonstrate that innovation is important;
- give a common cross-functional language which helps people to work together;
- ensure that ideas are properly evaluated and tested;
- ensure that implementation is planned for and executed well.

Example

Cummins Engines have given all their employees a programme on job and work analysis. Rather than leaving it solely to the expert function, they took the interesting view that it is everyone's responsibility to improve how he or she does his or her job, so they gave everyone the course. This has practical benefits in developing the competency, but it is also excellent for developing the commitment to an ever-improving, ever-changing organisation.

This set of skills and techniques should be open for all to dip into, from those concerned with incremental change at the operative level to the team which is building the ceramic engine or synthesising enzymes.

The kitbag has three key themes, though it would be a mistake to think of them as discrete. It is more helpful to regard them as areas of emphasis; indeed, several of the techniques follow two or even all three themes. These are:

- analysis;
- creativity;
- interpersonal behaviour.

They are all equally important, and they are interdependent. No matter how creative you are, if you cannot convert the ideas into practical reality and persuade the right people to back them, it is all to no avail.

A brief description of each technique is given under the appropriate heading (Table 7.3). For a full explanation and operating guidelines, readers can refer to the sources listed in the bibliography.

Table 7.3   The toolkit of techniques for the innovative organisation

Interpersonal behaviour	Creativity	Analysis
Group working	Creativity circles	Problem solving
Questioning and listening skills	Brainstorming	Evaluating alternatives
Assertiveness	Morphological analysis	Force-field analysis
'Mentoring'	Scenario writing	Data presentation
	Think tanks	Planning
	Suggestion schemes	Stakeholder analysis
	Creative thinking	Cost benefit analysis
		Job analysis
		Competitive benchmarking

Analytical techniques

Problem solving

We have been solving problems since we were children, so much so that now we tend to leap quite merrily from problem statement to solution, bypassing the real cause and indeed a clear definition of the problem. Companies need a common approach to solving problems: common throughout the company, so that irrespective of who is involved in the team, there is a common approach and language. How many arguments have you had recently about the 'how' of approaching a problem rather than the more familiar arguments about 'what' the solution is? A common and systematic approach also gives people confidence to voice their ideas, knowing that they will be treated seriously and evaluated in a understandable way rather than getting lost with the supervisor or in the suggestion box.

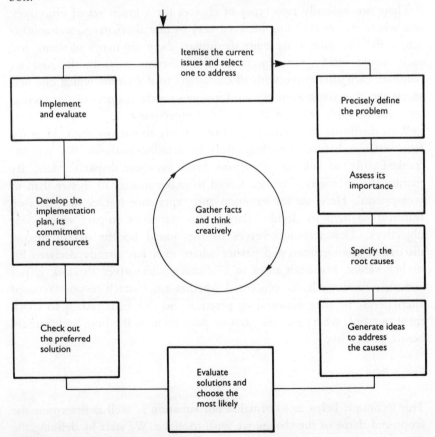

Fig. 7.3 A problem-solving framework

There are many variations of the problem-solving theme. One example is given in Fig. 7.3. Training establishes a common understanding of the steps and the techniques embodied within them, together with the building of skills and confidence.

Total quality programmes often have at their core a problem-solving process, as they recognise the importance of a shared approach to improving quality. This is in recognition of the need to replace 'shoot the messenger' with the notion that problems raised are good news because now we can solve them, and to focus attention on dealing with root causes rather than tinkering with symptoms.

Evaluating alternatives

Though also part of the problem-solving process, evaluating alternatives is something we do a great deal, even where there are no problems to solve: anywhere we have to make choices we are evaluating alternatives.

There are basically two types of choices for a given set of objectives: one where we are choosing between very similar alternatives, and another where the alternatives are quite dissimilar, there are many of them, and each would satisfy our objectives in a different way. In the first we compare each alternative with all the others to determine which one best meets the objectives. Here we tend to focus on the features of the alternatives which apply to the features of our objectives.

With dissimilar alternatives our aim is really to narrow the field in the first instance before investing effort in detailed analysis. We can use 'ranked pairs' to help us put a rank order on these disparate ideas. By pairing the alternatives we are forced to make choices of 'better than or worse than'. Here we use intuition and experience (rather than data on features) to help us decide relative importance or impact against our objectives. This technique gives us the added benefit of stimulating discussion among interested parties where each has already declared his or her views. For both cases of evaluating alternatives the task is not complete until we have considered whether risks attach to our favoured alternatives, be they financial or practical. So our final task is to check them out and, where possible, test or pilot them in the host environment before going 'live'.

Force-field analysis

This technique helps us to visualise our situation as well as determine the scope and shape of the change we wish to make. We start by defining the change in terms of where we want to be and where we are now. The

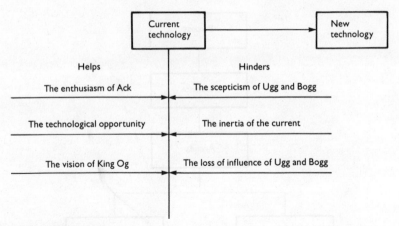

Fig. 7.4 Force-field analysis

process then requires us to identify the forces which are promoting the change and those which will restrain it. So often we just concentrate on the forces which will assist change and ignore those which will hold us back. The technique is based on the sound idea that change requires the promotion of the positive forces and the removal or minimisation of the counter-forces. Fig. 7.4 illustrates the technique using the case study example given on page 180.

Data presentation

Ideas, innovations and improvements must all be communicated well to persuade those with power and influence to make the necessary changes. Presenting data in an attractive and immediate way can go a long way towards convincing the powerful that the idea is sound.

Data presented visually is much more powerful than data presented through the written word. Line and bar charts, histograms, graphs, pie charts, diagrams and tables are all powerful ways in which we can make an immediate impact on those who have not been involved in the detail of our work.

Presentations themselves require planning and preparation to ensure that the point of delivery matches the power of our visual data. The key points to bear in mind in the preparation and the delivery of our material are outlined in Figs. 7.5 and 7.6.

Planning skills

Effective change has to be planned. A common language and set of planning techniques can provide a common basis on which multifunctional

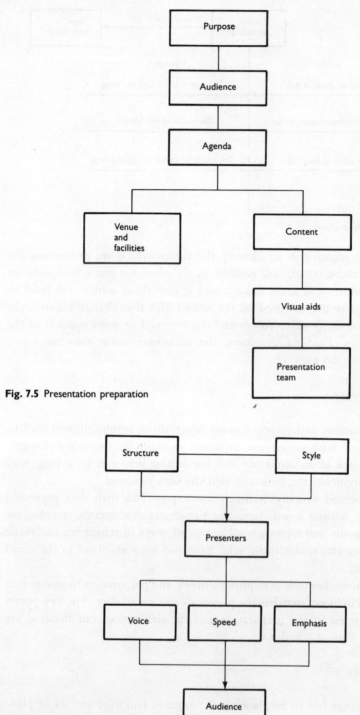

Fig. 7.5 Presentation preparation

Fig. 7.6 Presentation delivery

teams can manage change. Gantt charts and simple critical path analysis provide the means to map out the key steps over time to achieve the goal and are most helpful for straightforward changes. Where our changes are more complex, have many dimensions and higher degrees of uncertainty, then more complex systems such as computer-based multidimensional planning systems are required. The latter systems not only plan the constituent steps of a project but also plan the resources required to complete those steps. The project plan can thus be optimised for a range of single or multiple dimensions such as capital spend, labour or material availability. Some of the most sophisticated planning systems incorporate the dimension of risk in the planning process through using a series of probabilities or likelihoods that certain events will be completed in the time allocated.

Stakeholder analysis

Stakeholder analysis asks us to look at change in terms of the people who have a stake in the present and those who have a stake in the future. If we look at the Ugg and Bogg case study on page 180 in terms of stakeholders, it is clear that there is likely to be a major power shift if the new technology is adopted. How are those who have lost power going to feel and how are those who have gained power going to feel?

Stakeholder analysis is most helpful in working out who we have to convince that our innovation process will be protected until success or failure is final. The assessment of the 'stakes' that individuals have in both the present and the future can help us develop a workable plan.

Cost benefit analysis

The evaluation of ideas is a complex and sometimes uncertain process. Too often innovations are seen purely in terms of how much cost can be reduced by implementing the new technology. This is often cited as one of the great advantages of many information technology applications: that they appear to have immediate cost-saving benefits and very short payback times. Increasing product quality is far more difficult to cost and it is difficult to see the tangible benefit. Of concern to some organisations is the cost of *not* investing in a particular technology. In other words, the cost of not keeping up with our competitors is greater in the long run than doing so. This is difficult to justify in terms of a 'cost-saving' approach to financial investment.

An organisation which looks purely at technological innovation in narrow financial terms may well miss some of the greatest opportunities.

We can assist project analysis and evaluation through generating a common understanding of the criteria by which the organisation will consider new ideas. It is clearly pointless to encourage individuals to innovate if they do not understand, at least broadly, the criteria by which their ideas are likely to be accepted or rejected.

Cost benefit analysis therefore requires consideration of:

- typical cost factors (including time as a dimension);
- typical benefit factors (including non-financial benefits such as higher customer responsiveness);
- assumptions underlying the decision (such as the economic and market environment);
- the cost of not innovating.

Job analysis

In an innovative organisation everyone should be encouraged to analyse their own job, suggest improvements and work with others to effect overall change. A one-day course for all staff in the techniques of examining tasks and how to evaluate their effectiveness gives a new dimension to how individuals see their jobs.

In such a programme participants determine their 'customers', be they internal or external, clarify the output they deliver to these customers and the 'added value' they specifically contribute, and decide how they can enhance their flexibility to meet ever-changing customer demands.

An outcome of undertaking this form of job analysis is the focusing of all jobs towards the organisation's primary goals rather than towards functional or 'maintaining the system' goals.

Competitive benchmarking

We can often learn a great deal from the successful operations of other companies. It is common practice to compare the details of competitive products and services with those of our own. With our direct competitors we may also compare production and process technology. What is less common is the comparison of specific aspects of our organisation's activity with those of other organisations which we recognise as being particularly proficient in that part of their work, whether directly competitive or not.

The more innovative organisations, such as Rank Xerox, make competitive benchmarking a regular feature of their improvement process.

Creative techniques

Creativity circles

The emphasis on problem solving, performance improvement and quality circles has been one of responding to current issues and problems. Immediate problems need to be addressed, and the more participatively the better. Innovative companies need to build on this focus to move from problem-solving groups such as quality circles to creativity circles, where the emphasis is upon proactivity rather than dealing only with immediate problems and issues. It is a major step for a company to achieve the leap from reactivity to creativity. The concern is that in most organisations the vast majority, if not the totality, of management time is spent reacting. This results in people feeling lost, embarrassed and unable to think outside the bounds of their job demands.

In several companies where we have worked, small teams who are charged with looking into the future and coming up with ideas and proposals have made little progress. Many have struggled, as the freedom is so much out of their experience; they lack the confidence to have a 'blue-sky' thought. Perhaps those years of conformity take their toll. However, other organisations have much success with their 'breakthrough teams' or 'task forces' which have been set up to push out the boundaries of current operations.

Brainstorming

Brainstorming is a quick and effective means of producing a long list of ideas or potential solutions to problems. The simplicity of the process belies the potential pitfalls, the main one being our great urge to criticise the ideas of others, particularly if we see them as silly, stupid or downright irrelevant. This is a response on a personal level, and does not deal with the attributes or implications of the idea. The one guaranteed way to kill the effective use of brainstorming is for anyone, particularly the boss or leader, to give premature judgements, hence acting to belittle the originator of the idea. That will be the last idea you will get from that person.

The key rules are:

- Agree the issue or opportunity.
- Write it on a flip chart.
- Ask the group for all their ideas relating to that topic.
- Do not evaluate, discuss or react to any of the ideas until all have been generated.

- Review and refine the list.
- Evaluate the options using agreed criteria and an agreed process for evaluating alternatives.

Morphological analysis

Morphological analysis is another idea–generating technique. It produces a wide range of ideas for further exploration and quantification. It often starts with brainstorming, but has the added dimension of exploring the interrelatedness and combination of ideas. The analysis involves identifying the main parameters or functions of the issue and generating ideas under each parameter. Combinations of ideas are considered by placing each parameter on the axis of a matrix (Fig. 7.7). In a two-dimensional matrix, for example, a five by five matrix produces 25 ideas. Equally, the analysis can be done in three or more dimensions, though once we get beyond three a computer becomes an essential tool.

	Paper	Screen (VDU)	Three-dimensional	Clock	Calculator	Watch	Head-up display	Remote controlled vehicle	Models
Car									
Plane									
Boat									
Walker									
Geology									
Camper									
Ornithologist									
Cover the wall									
Meteorology									
Agriculture									
Tanks (military)									

Fig. 7.7 Morphological analysis – Potential applications for digital mapping.

Scenario writing

There are no techniques which will reliably predict the future. This, however, should not stop us identifying key trends and the factors which are most likely to influence our environment, market and products. In Western Europe we pride ourselves in having a multitude of economic forecasting models (usually predicting contrary outcomes) which attempt to identify key factors and trends in the economy and project how these may change over the coming years. Taken with knowledge of how accurate these tools are, they can give useful indicators for public policy and planning. The same idea applied to technology, products and the company's competitive position can give considerable insight for management who have a future orientation.

By analysing the present and identifying trends we can develop a range of scenarios suggesting where the organisation may be in five or ten years' time. This can be a valuable project for the young, aspiring manager whose thinking is not yet conditioned by 'group think' or 'experience'. If the scenarios are to be of real value it is essential that those undertaking these projects have a senior manager as a mentor to safeguard their freedom of thought and information, and to ensure the scenarios are considered in the company's formal business planning processes.

Think tanks

The idea of think tanks seems to have lost some of its attractions in the past few years as companies have sought to improve their short-term competitive positions. We again have a startling contrast between the incidence of think tanks in the UK and that in Japan. 'Lack of focus', 'unmeasurable impact' and 'expensive' are all criticisms which have been made of think tanks. For those companies which have to be leaders in their field the think tank is an important technique to ensure future market relevance. As turn-around times decrease the opportunity for companies to become followers diminishes. This is because once a new product is launched a competitor's lead time to imitate it is longer than the product's market life. By the time the imitation is on the market the original producer has brought out a more advanced model.

The think tank does not have to be a full-time commitment. A carefully chosen number of bright people from different parts of the organisation meeting one day per month can have a powerful influence upon a receptive management team.

Hitachi has a subsidiary company, the Hitachi Think Tank, employing between 70 and 80 people, of whom half are technologists and the remainder economists. The President of Hitachi is also President of the think tank.

Suggestion schemes

We looked at suggestion schemes in Chapter 6. Well-run schemes are not only a source of ideas but they also encourage an environment supportive of innovation.

Creative thinking

We have referred to the differences between right and left brain thinking, and the general lack of development of the right side of people's brains. There are various exercises which can stimulate creativity and overcome some of the barriers to creative thinking. We can identify some barriers merely by listening to how people respond to an idea:

- 'We tried that before.'
- 'It costs too much.'
- 'We're too small for that.'
- 'They'll never stand for this.'
- 'We don't have the authority.'
- 'You can't teach an old dog new tricks.'
- 'Let's give it more thought.'
- 'What you're really saying is . . .'
- 'Has anyone else ever tried it?'
- 'You just don't understand the problem.'
- 'It's against company policy.'
- 'That might work in your department, but it won't in mine.'
- 'It'll be too hard to sell.'
- 'Even the Japanese don't do that.'
- 'It's too radical.'
- 'A good thought, but impracticable.'
- 'Why change it? It works OK.'
- 'You're right, but . . .'
- 'Let's form a committee.'
- 'Let's shelve it for the time being.'
- 'Where did you dig that one up?'
- 'That's too ivory tower.'

Exercises which stimulate creative thinking ask us to find a solution to a seemingly impossible problem. The answers always lie outside the constraints of logical thinking. It is only when we abandon the patterns and inhibitions imposed upon us by our education and environment that we can see radically different ways of tackling a problem.

Example. Two creative thinking exercises
- Arrange ten dots into five straight rows of four dots each.
- A nurse was violently assaulted in a local hospital. As she was wheeled into the operating theatre she looked at the three surgeons who were present: Dr Murgatroyd, Dr Clark and Dr Welch. Although she was much too weak to point, she cried out, 'He did it. He attacked me'. She then lost consciousness. The police immediately arrested Dr Welch. How did they know that Dr Welch was the attacker?

In addition to the 'brain teasers', we can use such techniques as mind mapping and sets of challenging questions to prevent people from slipping into complacency, familiarity and tunnel vision.

Interpersonal techniques

Group working

Group working can be difficult. It may have as much to do with unlearning as with learning. We may have to unlearn how we manage at the moment if we currently rely heavily on our position in the organisation to get things done. This is positional power being used inappropriately and will not help either team working or problem solving. The skills of influencing through persuasion, collaboration and well thought-through ideas are of greater importance. We must also bear in mind that those not previously given responsibility or the opportunity to contribute ideas will have to unlearn old habits too, and gradually develop their competence in and commitment to a very different pattern of working (Fig. 7.8).

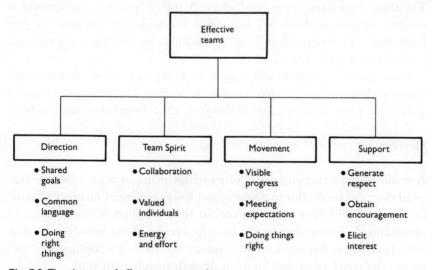

Fig. 7.8 The elements of effective group working

Questioning and listening skills

We exert our influence by effective questioning and listening skills, and this is particularly important where we are trying to sell a new idea or gain commitment for implementation. It is surprising the extent to which we expect others to see the value in our ideas as readily as we do.

Few individuals are either good questioners or good listeners. Much of our use of both techniques is based on the set of assumptions we carry with us. The problem is that most of us make different assumptions and this only becomes apparent once a decision has been made and our respective contributions to the implementation process do not fit.

Basically there are two types of question: open and closed. Open questions ask 'Who?', 'What?', 'Where?', 'When?', 'Why?' and 'How?' and closed questions demand a 'yes' or a 'no' response. It is important to consider whether you want a lengthy response, phrased in the respondent's own words, or a definitive answer.

Listening is an active process rather than the passive one it is often assumed to be. It requires us to *sense* the silent messages being sent by the speaker, often in the form of body language and tone of voice; to *attend* to the messages being sent by maintaining eye contact and making encouraging noises; and to *respond* by asking questions indicating our understanding of what the speaker has been saying.

Assertiveness

The timid may have some good ideas. A robust 'macho' management is unlikely to capture them. We can soften our style, but we also can give individuals a greater degree of confidence in putting forward and following through their ideas.

Being assertive is quite different from being aggressive. Assertiveness training demonstrates to participants how they can positively make a stance, put forward an opinion, or disagree, all without antagonising others.

Mentors

A mentor is an experienced and often senior manager who fulfils the role of adviser and counsellor to a young and less experienced member of staff. In some organisations this is an official role; in others it is informal and unstructured. Either way it can be effective for those members of staff who have ideas but no formal channels for their development. It also allows the more rapid development of such members of staff.

There are advantages too for the mentor, through the challenges and often open thinking of those with whom he or she comes into contact. In one organisation, young managers undertaking a company MBA were each given the task of analaysing and evaluating the effectiveness of a principal division or function. Their ideas and recommendations were given to the appropriate directors (their mentors), who were able to respond through specific improvement actions.

Summary

Organisations can be strongly influenced by the acceptance and development of appropriate training. There are both 'top-down' and 'bottom-up' elements of such training. The top-down training is the extent to which the organisation places a priority on and provides resources for training and provides a learning environment in which the creative can flourish. As we have indicated, there are considerable advantages in giving everyone in an organisation a common language and a set of basic techniques which encourage incremental improvement.

The bottom-up element is that we cannot enforce creativity or indeed learning: management having provided the basic grounding and resources, and created the environment, individuals need to be able to use the learning according to their own capabilities.

The key questions for managers are:

- What proportion of training and development expenditure is focused on innovation and creativity?
- Do you train your managers to manage complex change processes?
- Do training activities have high credibility in your organisation?

References

1. *First* magazine, Memorandum, **2** (2) 1988. *The Human Side of Acquisitions and Mergers*, London Business School, 1988
2. Twiss, B. (1985) Non MSC Research and Initiatives in the Field of Management Development for Technical Change. MSC.
3. Arthur Young International *The 'Focus' Approach to Business Strategy Development.*
4. Peters, T. J. and Waterman, R. H. (1982) *In Search of Excellence*. Harper and Row.
5. Ibid.
6. Northcott, J. et al (1985) *Promoting Innovation: Microelectronics Applications Projects*. PSI.
7. 'In Search of Excellence'. Melrose Films.
8. Hickman, C. R. and Silva, M. A. (1985) *Creating Excellence: Managing Corporate Culture, Strategy and Change in the New Age*. George Allen and Unwin.
9. Gunn, T. G. (1987) *Manufacturing for Competitive Advantage*, Ballinger.

8 The technical change programme

In this final chapter we shall draw together the threads of the arguments discussed earlier in the book and present a systematic approach whereby a company can analyse its own needs for technical change and ensure that the changes identified are implemented effectively.

The pervasiveness of technology is such that it affects *all* companies, including many for which it has not been a concern in the past; this is particularly true of the service sector. For many companies technological innovation is the main source of competitive advantage, which can be fully exploited only through major organisational changes. But for others it may be a peripheral concern, although well-managed changes may provide a valuable edge in a highly competitive market. Thus there are no universal prescriptions. Nevertheless, we would claim that in all cases the technical change cannot be introduced without consideration of what organisational changes may be needed to ensure success.

The managerial dilemma

Throughout our discussions we have tended to draw comparisons between two classes of company: the stable and the innovative. The stable company operates in a mature market and has fashioned its organisation and managerial systems to do a well-defined job efficiently. It has a good appreciation of its business environment, which in the past has evolved slowly, a hierarchical organisational structure with decisions concentrated at the top and formal managerial systems. It has little experience of introducing radical changes and, when they are forced upon it, it is usually not capable of implementing them effectively. At the other extreme we have the innovative organisation where change is the norm. It is dynamic, entrepreneurial and informal in its managerial style.

For most companies this polarisation is unrealistic. Much of their business now and for the foreseeable future will come from their established products, services and markets. Technical change for them consists in the incorporation of new manufacturing systems or management systems into the business without a major modification to the nature of its output. At the same time they have to develop some new activities to supplement or replace the existing businesses as they face the inevitability of decline in the long term. Other companies may need to change continuously, but the rate of change is such that it may be inappropriate to fashion themselves on the archetypal innovative firm. However, few, if any, companies are likely to succeed in the future without adopting many of the features of the innovative company. Nevertheless, many elements of the stable company may still be appropriate. The dilemma lies in designing the right mix between these contrasting styles of management.

Another problem arises with deciding upon the rate of change. Where change is necessary it will occur. Experience shows that this frequently happens as a result of outside intervention, for example a take-over or the appointment of a new chief executive. This is often accompanied by plant closures, redundancies and senior management changes, inevitably a painful process. The fact that many companies survive this disruption indicates that within them there is an inherent potential which had previously been unexploited. This supports the findings of our research, which revealed an understanding of what was needed at many levels of the organisations we studied. In the right circumstances that potential can be released. The challenge for an existing management is to bring about these changes in an organic fashion and with the minimum of disruption.

In doing this it is necessary to formulate a strategy for introducing change based upon:

- a clear understanding of the technical and organisational objectives – where they want to be eventually;
- a time scale and plan for achieving the objectives – how quickly they can get there;
- a phased plan for introducing specific technical and organisational changes and training for their achievement.

It is also useful to draw a distinction between the two levels at which technology might change the business: the strategic and the operational. At the strategic level it may be found necessary to introduce some fundamental changes in the concept of what the business is, a redefinition based upon some of the considerations discussed in Chapter 1. At the operational level the concern is the implementation of technical and organisational change within the business, whether or not there is a strategic change of emphasis. The first is largely based upon an analysis of external factors, the latter on internal.

The innovative company

Before considering how a company can approach technical change in a systematic fashion it is worth noting the most important features of the innovative firm, which we have identified in earlier chapters. These are:

- sensitivity to trends in the total business environment;
- a long-term orientation;
- top management commitment to change;
- cross-functional integration;
- a high level of communications, both top-down and bottom-up;
- flexibility to enable a rapid response;
- an external orientation;
- creativity and a responsiveness to new ideas;
- the presence and encouragement of internal entrepreneurs;
- responsibility for all aspects of a change programme vested in one person;
- identification, capture and transfer of new knowledge;
- a focus on user needs and receptivity to user ideas;
- investment in education and training to support the change.

The creation of the right environment for the generation and implementation of technical change to incorporate these features can be seen to be dependent upon a number of interrelating elements:

- corporate culture;
- the processes of strategy formulation and dissemination;
- the organisational structure;
- managerial information and control systems;
- the attitudes, motivations and contributions of individuals.

If a change programme does not address all these elements it is unlikely to realise its full potential.

The analysis of technical change needs

In the following sections we list a range of questions which provide a framework to enable senior managers to analyse their current position, identify areas of desirable change and plan for their implementation. This is based upon a series of workshops conducted with senior managers of a number of companies in different sectors of business. It provides a systematic approach to a consideration of the totality of the programme against a background of the concepts introduced earlier. It cannot predicate what actions should be taken in relation to a particular company; only that company's management can make the necessary judgements.

Several observations can be made from the experience of using this approach. Most importantly, it ensures that the total organisational implications of introducing technical change are examined explicitly. It provides a mechanism for involving the senior management from all functions in an open debate. The authors and the participants have been surprised by the high degree of consensus revealed by the discussions. It has enabled the participants to express personal views which they did not believe to be widely shared by others, only to find that they too had been thinking along the same lines.

The analysis is of little value if it does not lead to managerial decisions and actions. This is the most difficult, but also the most important, aspect of the exercise. Having identified areas for improvement, there is a tendency to focus attention on all of them simultaneously. Whilst this may appear desirable, it is likely to lead to a diffusion of effort within the limited managerial resources that can be devoted to it. Thus the establishment of priorities is essential and, as with all plans, these must be associated with a time scale for implementation. A sense of urgency is needed, whilst taking heed of the pace at which change can realistically be absorbed by the organisation. The question must be asked: 'What do we do tomorrow?'. Attention must also be paid to how the change programme can be disseminated and to how others can be involved in the detail of the planning.

Although much effort is devoted to analysing both the external and the internal environments, the competition should not be overlooked. In many areas one cannot derive absolute values for the answers. That is not important. What is important is how the company measures up to its competition.

The structure of the analysis

The total process leading to the successful management of technical change is illustrated in Fig. 8.1. It starts with an analysis of the company as it presently exists by means of three audits: cultural, innovation and technical. This gives an understanding of the receptivity of change within the company culture, how this is reflected within the organisation by its organisational structure, systems and management styles, and its technical ability.

The next step is to assess the environment of the business in order to evaluate the extent to which technical change is needed to meet the company's objectives. This leads to a consideration of the degree of

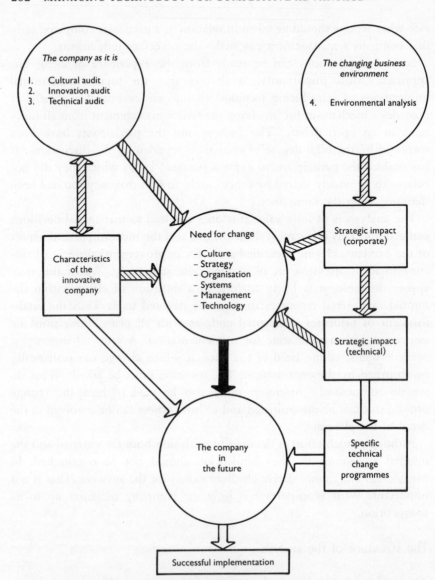

Fig. 8.1 The structure of the technical change analysis

strategic change which may be required and, within that, the need for a change in the technical strategy.

These analyses will be conducted against the background of the characteristics of the innovative firm as discussed earlier in the book. Thus the audit exercise leads logically to an examination of what changes must be made within the company to create the conditions whereby specific technical change programmes can be implemented successfully. It is then possible to construct a scenario of what the company might look like at some time in the future from which an action plan for the path to be followed to the desired end point can be formulated. This action plan must be comprehensive but realistic. It takes time to introduce organisational changes in a way which is acceptable to those responsible for implementing them.

The cultural audit

The term 'corporate culture' has been used to describe the underlying values and attitudes which, although largely implicit, determine the unwritten criteria that run through all major company decisions. It is essential to give a sense of coherence to what the company is, its values, its aspirations and how it conducts its business. This culture will have evolved over time and in the absence of severe external pressures is likely to evolve only slowly, if at all. However, as we have seen, this source of past strength may contain a fatal flaw if it is no longer appropriate to the competitive needs of the company.

Innovation flourishes within a different type of corporate culture from that found in more stable and change-averse organisations. A competitive analysis may lead to the realisation that a company needs to innovate. To a great extent this is an intellectual assessment, but, however well conceived, the innovations are unlikely to succeed fully if the internal corporate climate is not in harmony with them. Thus any consideration of change must commence with some assessment of these values, even if it is likely to lack precision. If there is a major mismatch between the two it may be necessary to change the culture or seek non-innovative solutions within the existing culture. In many of the organisations studied by the authors it has become evident that, however pressing the needs for change, and despite the fact that often there is a recognition of these needs, there has been a culture sufficiently unsympathetic to innovation to make the chance of success remote.

Cultural change is by its very nature a sensitive topic. No outside consultant can stipulate what a company's culture should be. This is a matter of values and attitudes that only top management can determine. Nevertheless, an assessment of the culture must be the logical starting point for any examination of technical change. Some of the factors to be considered will now be briefly discussed and are summarised in the form of a profile chart (Fig. 8.2) which helps management to visualise their own perceptions. Because of the difficulty of discussing these topics in the abstract it has been found useful to consider them in relation to the

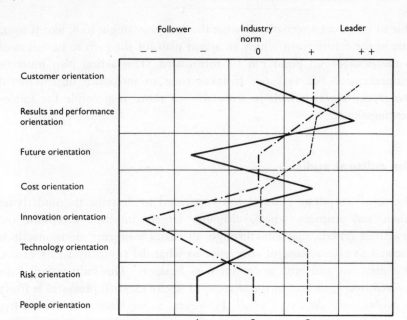

A: Present position
B: Position in three years without change
C: Desired position in three years

Fig. 8.2 Cultural orientation profile chart

competition in order to gain a relative judgement. It is also worth giving some consideration to the desired situation at some time in the future to gain an understanding of the gap between the present and what may be required. This is a rough indication of the need for cultural change and the direction it should take. Because these perceptions may change as more detailed factors are examined, it is recommended that the initial assessment is re-examined at the conclusion of the study.

- *Whom do you regard as the pacemaker in your industry and why?* In most industries there is a recognised leader. Some discussion of the charac-teristics of this leader provides a useful backcloth against which one's own company can be assessed.
- *Customer orientation* represents the value which is placed upon the customers, knowledge of the customers and their problems, contacts and relationships with them and the quality of service.
- *Results and performance orientation* is a reflection of the importance attached to the setting of objectives, the aggressiveness in achieving them and their role in assessing managerial performance.
- *Future orientation* is the extent to which there is a 'vision of the future', the emphasis placed on examining the long-term future of the business

in relation to its strategy, products and services, and the technology to support or develop them. This may lead to an examination of whether there are any inconsistencies between this and the previous factor.

- *Cost orientation* relates to the priority accorded to the reduction of production or service costs as the determinant of competitive advantage. It may also reflect a focus on operational efficiency.
- *Innovation orientation* represents the value attached to change rather than incremental development of products, operational and managerial systems and organisation.
- *Technology orientation* is the importance attributed to technology as providing the basis for competitiveness and as a consideration in the formulation of strategy.
- *Risk orientation* is the willingness to accept losses on activities which have a lower than average probability of success but a potentially high return on the investment if successful.
- *People orientation* represents the extent to which employees are regarded as individual contributors to the success of the business as distinct from their role as performers of tightly specified tasks, and the extent of the investment in training and development.

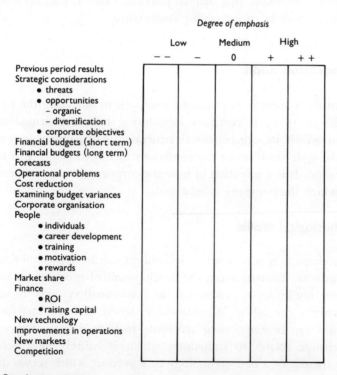

Fig. 8.3 Boardroom priorities

None of these orientations is inherently good or bad. The profile merely represents the perceptions of the managers involved and provides an agenda for debate. However, that debate may also reveal that some of the initial views are inconsistent.

A broad indication of the culture can also be obtained from an examination of those concerns which dominate the attention of the top management. One way in which this can be done is by an assessment of the emphasis placed on a number of considerations during board discussions. Some idea of this is obtainable from an examination of the agenda and the minutes of board meetings. It is, however, much more desirable to obtain the opinions of those involved by means of a questionnaire completed after a discussion (Fig. 8.3). Although the items are listed in a random order they can be broadly categorised as:

- short term *v.* long term;
- internally *v.* externally orientated;
- problem solving *v.* opportunity seeking.

In a non-innovative company it is likely that the discussions will focus on the short term, internal considerations and problem solving. Whilst all the topics deserve attention, this analysis provides valuable insights into those aspects deemed to be of overriding importance.

The innovation audit

The innovation audit is a systematic approach to analysing the extent to which the company is currently introducing technical change and the degree to which its organisational structure, management systems and managerial style conform to the conditions identified as being conducive to innovation. It is a reflection of how the corporate culture influences the way in which the company is managed.

The technological profile

In earlier chapters it was seen that technology can be applied in four areas of the business: diversification, the development of products (or services) for the existing business, production (or operational) systems, or management systems (including information systems). Within each area the innovations can be categorised according to their degree of novelty. A radical change relates to something which is entirely new because it involves the use of a new technology or a product which serves different customer needs or satisfies current needs in a novel fashion. The next

Extent of change \ Type of change	Diversification	Product/ Service	Production/ Operations	Management Systems
New (radical)	now / future	/	/	/
New (without major change)	/	/	/	/
Improved (incremental)	/	/	/	now / future

Insert numbers to indicate degree of emphasis

None	Low	Medium		High	
0	1	2	3	4	5

Fig. 8.4 Technological profile analysis

category still involves a degree of novelty without breaking entirely new ground. It might be a new model to replace existing products within the conventional configuration. The final category is an incremental improvement to enhance performance without change to the basic design.

The matrix in Fig. 8.4 provides a format for assessing the current situation. The weightings may be derived judgementally or from the level of investment in each category if the figures are available.

Figure 8.5 shows how the technology profile analysis can be used to identify the need for technological change both now and in the future. The present situation is assessed by inserting numbers above the diagonal line in the matrix to indicate the current emphasis. This may or may not be appropriate to the needs of the current product portfolio, which can be

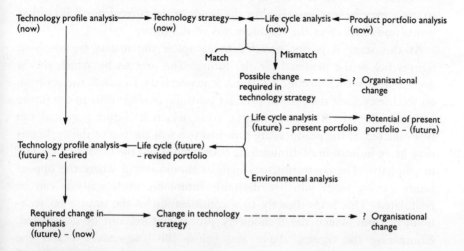

Fig. 8.5 Identification of change in technological strategy

Current product portfolio (now)				D C B A		
Current product portfolio (future)					D C B A	
Desired product portfolio (future)		F E		D C B		

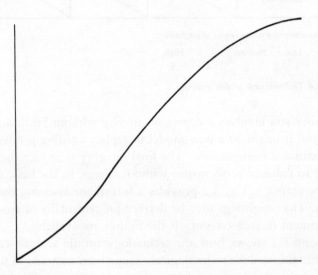

Fig. 8.6 Life cycle analysis

determined by considering where the products lie on the technology/industry life cycle (Fig. 8.6). If there is a mismatch it indicates that the technical strategy may be inappropriate for the needs of the current portfolio unless it is already reflecting the requirements of the future.

At this stage it is not possible to complete the matrix by inserting figures below the diagonal for the future. The process by which this is done is also shown in Fig. 8.6. First it is necessary to assess the position on the life cycle of the present product portfolio at some time in the future (possibly three to five years hence), from which its future potential can be evaluated. If the products are bunched towards the top of the cycle this may be an indication of diminishing profitability and the need for a change in emphasis. The environmental analysis should reveal where the opportunities exist, from which a desirable future life cycle analysis can be postulated. This leads directly to a consideration of the impact on technology, from which the technology profile (future) can be completed. Comparing the figures above and below the diagonals indicates the required changes in the technology strategy to satisfy these needs. In order to implement the revised strategy, organisational changes are likely to be required, but these cannot be assessed until the later stages in the innovation audit have been completed.

The organisational profile

The organisational profile provides a means of assessing the internal activities by which the company deploys its resources and controls its operations in order to achieve its corporate objectives. In its broader context it comprises all those tasks we understand as management.

Before considering these aspects in detail it is worth drawing a distinction between the words 'effectiveness' and 'efficiency' (see also Chapter 2). Effectiveness is concerned with the output, how well the resources deployed in the company contribute to the achievement of the strategic aims. Efficiency focuses on the internal operations and the elimination of waste. Every organisation should strive to be both effective and efficient. However, it must be appreciated that these two aims can on occasions become inconsistent. In order to achieve efficiency one needs measures against which the operations can be evaluated. This can lead to managerial effort being directed towards those factors which can be measured easily and exercising control in relation to them whether or not they contribute to the achievement of the corporate objectives. Thus a manager may be assessed in relation to his or her ability to operate within the cost budget rather than on what he or she achieves with the resources, or creative individuals may be assessed on their attendance record rather than on the quality of their ideas. In the final analysis it is effectiveness which is important, and it must be recognised that whilst efficiency is also highly desirable, it should not become an end in itself if it distracts attention from output objectives. For many aspects of technical change it is impossible to establish quantitative measures of efficiency, and attempts to do so may be unrealistic. Thus it is useful to examine whether the company's practices and managerial behaviour are focused on achieving effectiveness or efficiency.

The analysis of the organisational profile is aimed at assessing the current situation in relation to:

- the perceived corporate role of technical change;
- the organisational structure;
- the formal management systems;
- the informal managerial processes.

The role of technical change

This explores a number of questions (Fig. 8.7) which enable top and senior management to assess their perceptions of the importance currently accorded to technical change in relation to the achievement of their corporate objectives, its effectiveness and the factors which encourage or inhibit it. This complements the technology profile in that it is directed towards gaining an insight into the attitudes of management towards technical change, whereas the technical profile was confined to strategic considerations.

The organisational structure

This defines the formal relationships within the company normally needed to serve the requirements of running the existing business and facilitating change. The former often involves a relatively low level of interfunctional communication and lends itself to the high degree of centralisation, job definition and specialisation found within a hierarchical structure. In contrast, we have seen that technical change demands a high level of interfunctional communication, flexibility and delegation of decision making. At the extreme this can be achieved by a venture group structure, but in most situations some form of compromise, such as a matrix structure, is necessary. The incorporation of the requirements for technical change within an ongoing operation is one of the most difficult problems to resolve satisfactorily; there is no ideal solution. In many companies, however, the effective implementation of technical change is inhibited by the emphasis placed upon the vertical orientation of a hierarchical structure. The correct balance to be struck depends upon the nature of the company and the extent of the technical change. Whilst no prescriptions can be laid down for the balance between the contrasting sets of requirements, consideration of them should not be ignored. Some of these considerations are listed in Fig. 8.8.

It must be stressed that at this stage in the analysis there should be no attempt to evaluate the appropriateness of the existing structure. The aim is to establish the characteristics of the company at the present time. Only later, after all the audits are completed, can attention be directed towards a consideration of what structure might be more appropriate and the extent to which changes in the organisation are desirable.

Formal management systems

Within the organisational structure there are a number of systems to

	Importance rating				
	Low		Medium		High
	0	1	2	3	4	5

1. The future success of the business depends upon:
   (a) improving operational efficiency
   (b) diversification
   (c) capital investment
   (d) new products or services
   (e) people
   (f) external factors outside our control
   (g) tighter managerial controls
   (h) ability to respond rapidly to external pressures
2. The contribution of technical change in the past has been:
3. The effectiveness of technical change programmes has been:
4. The degree to which technical change has been associated with organisational change has been:
5. Technical change is limited by:
   (a) availability of finance
   (b) difficulty in evaluating its worth
   (c) past failures
   (d) management resistance
   (e) worker or trade union resistance
   (f) shortage of good ideas
   (g) shortage of skills
   (h) poor project management
   (i) lack of technical know-how
6. The purpose of technical change has been to:
   (a) reduce operational costs
   (b) maintain product competitiveness
   (c) sustain corporate growth
   (d) improve management efficiency
7. Ideas for technical change come from:
   (a) top management
   (b) technical departments
   (c) other internal sources
   (d) strategic analysis
   (e) outside sources
8. The receptiveness of *technical* change by:
   (a) senior managers
   (b) middle managers
   (c) supervisors
   (d) workers
   (e) trade unions
9. The receptiveness of *organisational* change by:
   (a) senior managers
   (b) middle managers
   (c) supervisors
   (d) workers
   (e) trade unions
10. The company encourages:
    (a) creativity
    (b) individual initiative
    (c) risk taking
    (d) participation in idea generation
    (e) participation in decision making
    (f) training
    (g) job rotation
    (h) job specifications
    (i) individual performance objectives
    (j) individual performance incentives
    (k) conformity to company norms
11. Technical change programmes owe their origins to:
    (a) corporate objectives
    (b) technical initiatives
    (c) market or user needs
    (d) operational problem solving

Fig. 8.7 Perceptions of the role of technical change

		Yes	No
1.	The current organisational structure within which technical change takes place is:		
	(a) hierarchical		
	(b) venture group		
	(c) matrix		
	(d) project management		
	(e) a combination		
2.	The current organisational structure:		
	(a) facilitates technical change		
	(b) causes disruption to the ongoing operations		
3.	Technical change is		
	(a) the responsibility of an interfunctional committee		
	(b) developed sequentially, with management passing from one function to another as the project advances		
	(c) vested in one person		
4.	The project manager (where appointed):		
	(a) reports to top management		
	(b) reports to departmental management		
	(c) reports to an interdepartmental committee		
	(d) has total business responsibility		
	(e) has total technical responsibility		
	(f) is a coordinator		
	(g) controls his or her own budget		
	(h) provides information to decision makers		
5.	The following are involved at all stages:		
	(a) top management		
	(b) technical departments		
	(c) finance		
	(d) operations/production		
	(e) marketing		
	(f) personnel		
	(g) training		
	(h) customers/users		
6.	The following are involved at *some* stage:		
	(a) top management		
	(b) technical departments		
	(c) finance		
	(d) operations/production		
	(e) marketing		
	(f) personnel		
	(g) customers/users		

Fig. 8.8 Organisational structure profile

ensure that managerial decisions conform to company policies and to provide a standardised format for departmental decision making. Each function is supported by its own systems and by the overall corporate communication system. To a great extent these are likely to mirror the hierarchical or departmental organisational structure and are designed to meet the needs of decision making in relation to:

- technology;
- finance;
- marketing;
- operations/production;
- personnel and training.

It has been seen in earlier chapters that a technical change cuts across many, if not all, of these systems. Ideally from the viewpoint of the project manager he or she should be able to acquire and deploy the resources he or she needs without hindrance from those company policies which have been formulated to serve a different purpose. Furthermore, the project manager requires an information system which provides what he or she needs in a form which enables him or her to take timely and appropriate decisions. With the exception of a venture group organisation, where the project manager is in effect highly autonomous, these requirements will not be fully met. A compromise solution must be sought in which the following considerations must be taken into account:

- the *integration* across each of the systems whereby the implications of a change to one part of it is assessed in relation to the totality of that system, e.g. the impact of a change of materials on the manufacturing process;
- the *interaction* between systems whereby the effect of a change in the technical system may affect other systems, e.g. the reward system;
- the *identification of barriers* to technical change imposed by the formal system, e.g. the ability to recruit key people.

In deciding what changes should be introduced into the management systems to achieve these objectives there are three main alternatives:

(a) To devise systems which meet the needs of both technical change and the ongoing operations. This is the most desirable approach, but may require radical organisational changes the company is unwilling to introduce.

(b) To maintain the existing systems with minor amendments, but to introduce sufficient flexibility into them to allow departures from the established practice in exceptional cases, for example the sanctioning of the appointment of outstanding individuals outside the normal payment structure.

(c) To leave the systems unchanged and hope that the ingenuity of the project manager will enable him or her to circumvent the barriers. This imposes a great strain on the informal processes (discussed later) and, although commonplace, is not desirable.

The problems can be addressed by designing the formal systems so that they serve the needs of technical change whatever form it may take or by ensuring that they are examined in relation to the needs of a specific change programme. In both cases the aspects to be considered are similar. Many of them have already been discussed.

Figure 8.9 lists some of the most important systems in each functional area found in all companies and illustrates their impact on the technical

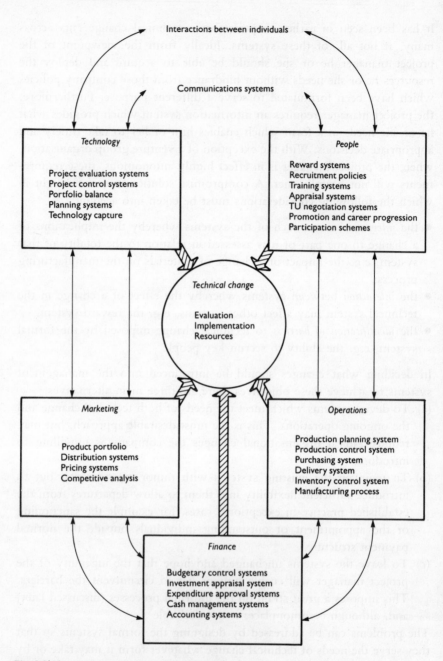

Interactions between individuals

Communications systems

Technology

Project evaluation systems
Project control systems
Portfolio balance
Planning systems
Technology capture

People

Reward systems
Recruitment policies
Training systems
Appraisal systems
TU negotiation systems
Promotion and career progression
Participation schemes

Technical change

Evaluation
Implementation
Resources

Marketing

Product portfolio
Distribution systems
Pricing systems
Competitive analysis

Operations

Production planning system
Production control system
Purchasing system
Delivery system
Inventory control system
Manufacturing process

Finance

Budgetary control systems
Investment appraisal system
Expenditure approval systems
Cash management systems
Accounting systems

Fig. 8.9 Management systems and technical change

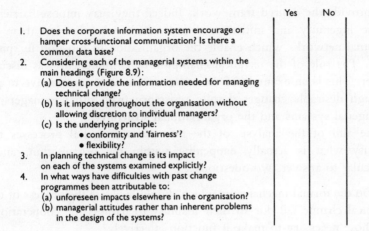

		Yes	No
1.	Does the corporate information system encourage or hamper cross-functional communication? Is there a common data base?		
2.	Considering each of the managerial systems within the main headings (Figure 8.9):		
	(a) Does it provide the information needed for managing technical change?		
	(b) Is it imposed throughout the organisation without allowing discretion to individual managers?		
	(c) Is the underlying principle:		
	• conformity and 'fairness'?		
	• flexibility?		
3.	In planning technical change is its impact on each of the systems examined explicitly?		
4.	In what ways have difficulties with past change programmes been attributable to:		
	(a) unforeseen impacts elsewhere in the organisation?		
	(b) managerial attitudes rather than inherent problems in the design of the systems?		

Fig. 8.10 Technical change and management systems analysis

change programme. Integration is achieved by both the formal corporate communication systems and the informal interactions between individuals. This diagram provides a basis for discussing the needs of technical change in which the questions in Fig. 8.10 can be considered.

Informal managerial processes

The organisational structure and the formal managerial systems, however well they are designed, cannot specify in every detail the communications needed between individuals so that they can perform their managerial roles effectively. This depends upon a web of interpersonal relationships. Although it may be possible to design a structure and systems to meet the corporate needs, these will not function without the cooperation of those involved. It is they who provide the information a communication system processes. For example, one of the most frequently cited short-comings of the operation of sophisticated information systems is the failure to ensure that the information fed into it is kept up to date: a personal responsibility. It is the meeting of minds that is the basis of an integrated approach to a problem. An information system may provide the framework within which this integration can take place, but it will not function effectively without human cooperation. Thus a project evaluation system may involve contributions from several functions, but it will not achieve its desired objective without a genuine integration of the views of the managers involved in it: the system itself cannot guarantee that this will occur.

There are many occasions, however, when the formal approaches do not provide the desired framework. Indeed they may impose barriers. It is the ingenuity and initiative of individuals who develop their own informal networks which enable the organisation to function in spite of itself. The role of the technical champion or entrepreneur was discussed earlier. This is an example of the exercise of individual initiative to push through desirable changes despite resistance from other managers, the managerial systems and the organisational structure.

The aim of the analysis of the informal managerial processes is to identify what is actually happening within the organisation, and in particular to answer two questions:

(a) Do the formal mechanisms which should facilitate the process of technical change fail due to their inability to harness the cooperation of those necessary to make it function effectively?
(b) What processes exist whereby technical change is effected in spite of deficiencies in the formal mechanisms?

The matrix in Fig. 8.11 illustrates these alternatives, from which it can be seen that attention must be directed not only towards the design of the formal approaches – an enabling mechanism – but also to the way in which they are used – the operation of the systems in practice.

In assessing the processes one is trying to identify what is actually happening in the organisation as distinct from what, in the view of its designers, ought to happen. Ideally both formal and informal processes should be harnessed to the same end. Where they diverge the reasons must be identified and analysed to establish whether this is a consequence of poor management within the formal systems or of managerial responses

		Informal managerial processes (human)	
		Good informal networks (communication and integration)	Poor informal networks (isolationist)
Formal framework (structure and systems)	Supportive of technical change	A Condition for effective technical change	B Poor implementation of technical change
	Inhibits technical change	C Occasional technical change dependent on individual effort	D Technical change unlikely

Fig. 8.11 Formal v. informal processes

1. How important are informal processes in the company?
   (a) Why?
   (b) Are they encouraged/discouraged?
   (c) Are they desirable/undesirable?

2. Vertical communications: top-down. How is knowledge of strategic objectives and policies disseminated throughout the company?
   (a) What is the process?
   (b) Which people are involved in the process?
   (c) How does it occur?
   (d) Is there sufficient information?
   (e) Is there a commitment to communicate?

3. Vertical communications: bottom-up. To what extent do all employees become involved in passing knowledge up through the organisation?
   (a) What are the processes?
   (b) Who makes the most important contributions?
   (c) Is the full potential exploited?
   (d) Is there active participation?
   (e) Is there commitment?

4. Horizontal communications.
   (a) To what extent do managers in different functions communicate?
      • within the formal system?
      • outside the formal systems?
   (b) Who are the most active communicators in each function? What form does their communication take?
   (c) By what process is knowledge gained of:
      • users needs?
      • technical information (e.g. gatekeepers)?

5. Political processes.
   (a) In discussion do individuals:
      • seek the optimum corporate solution?
      • support proposals which further their individual or departmental interests?
      • withhold information?
      • admit errors openly?
   (b) Do individuals form pressure groups:
      • to protect their own power or status?
      • to oppose change?
      • Who are those people?

6. Technical change.
   (a) How important is the informal role of:
      • creative individuals?
      • champions or entrepreneurs?
      • unauthorised initiatives (e.g. user innovations)?
   (b) By what means do technical change agents gain support?

Fig. 8.12 Analysis of informal processes

to overcome inherent weaknesses in those systems. Some of the questions which direct attention to these issues are listed in Fig. 8.12.

The technical audit

Earlier in this chapter we discussed technology in respect of its current strategy (the technology profile analysis) and the perceived role of technical change in the organisation. The technical audit is concerned with assessing the technical capabilities in terms of what has been achieved in the past and its current potential. These may or may not be adequate for supporting its existing corporate role. However, if a major extension of this role in the future is thought necessary it is likely that changes will also be required in the resources devoted to it in quantity and type, and in the way in which they are managed. Thus it is necessary to identify areas of strength and weakness in relation to not only the present but also the future.

In general it is desirable to build upon strength. However, in relation to technology a present strength may often translate into a weakness for the future. Competence in a technology of declining importance represented by its human and physical assets may then become a liability. This is particularly true of the human resources, where it can take a considerable time to acquire the expertise and the people and to weld them into an effective team, combined with a reluctance to shed staff whose expertise is no longer relevant.

It can be expected that there will be some understanding of the future needs, although they cannot be specified in detail without an environmental analysis and an assessment of the strategic emphasis. This must be an iterative process, since there is no merit in formulating an ambitious strategy if the capabilities for its successful implementation do not exist or are unlikely to be made available.

A starting point must be the size of the investment made in technology, bearing in mind what the competition is doing. This can at best be only a rough guide, since it is an input measure and gives no indication of how well the investment has been utilised. In many areas of technology it is almost impossible to devise meaningful output measures. For example, there have been numerous studies into measuring R&D effectiveness, but the results have been inconclusive. Usually the measures suggested relate to outputs such as the number of patents registered, which may bear little relationship to their commercial potential. Nevertheless, it is of some value to compare the technical investment with that of competitors in so far as this can be estimated both in absolute terms and as a percentage of turnover. Any major discrepancy indicates that there may be a strong case for reviewing the company's investment in technology.

The main headings under which the technical audit should be undertaken are listed in Fig. 8.13. In order to make the assessments it is desirable that a more detailed investigation be undertaken addressing some of the questions raised in earlier chapters. The second column (entitled Technological Capital for the Future) evaluates the current capabilities in relation to the possible technical strategies derived later. Any significant gaps between the two profiles indicate areas where change must be in-

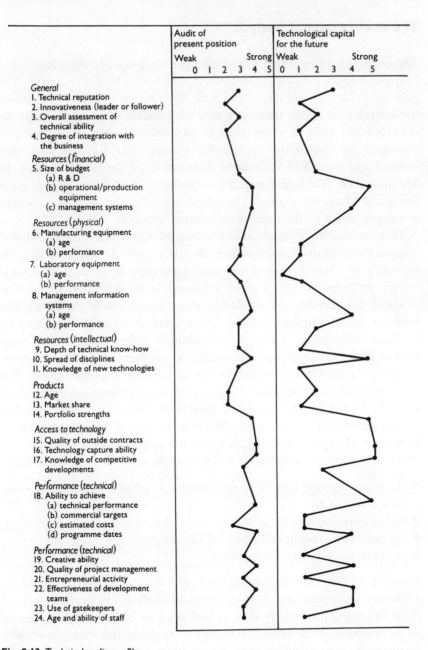

Fig. 8.13 Technical audit profile

troduced into the technical activities if the strategy is to be achieved, or even indicate the inadvisability of embarking upon a particular strategy because of a low probability that it can be implemented effectively.

The environmental analysis

The environment in which a business operates is always changing. Some of these changes are cyclical and others represent a long-term trend. It is essential to identify and respond to both. Because the trends often manifest themselves over a long time scale they are difficult to assess, and may be imperceptible over a short period, particularly when their effect is swamped by short-term cyclical fluctuations. Yet for the long-term survival and growth of a company these can be of critical significance. In addition there are occasional discontinuities which can be the most important of all, for example the emergence of a new technology which is a major threat to the company's existing products.

There is usually a good understanding of the major trends within a company's collective consciousness. In many cases, however, it may be necessary to conduct detailed forecasts or purchase them from an outside agency in order to gain a more informed view. Although it must be accepted that forecasts are unreliable, some assessment of the future as a basis for decision making is unavoidable. Managerial judgement must be the final determinant, but it is more soundly based when it takes cognisance of the best information available in a systematic fashion. In practice the main problem is not the identification of the important trends, but in assessing the time scale over which they will occur and the reluctance of management to take action on what they believe to be the case but cannot prove conclusively until often it is too late. Thus it is valuable to learn from the trends and experience of the past and assess how they are likely to evolve in the future in order to evaluate how they will affect:

• the main strategic focuses of the business in relation to both opportunities and threats;
• the relative importance of the resources deployed in the business;
• the needs of existing and potential customers;
• strength vis-a-vis the competition.

Figure 8.14 lists the major headings and questions which should be addressed in conducting an environmental analysis. In practice each of these headings, particularly item 4, will need to be expanded in relation to the situation of the individual company. In doing this many trends will be revealed, most of which may already be incorporated implicitly in the company's existing plans. The purpose of the exercise should be to identify those, usually few in number, which are of critical importance and which require a major change in some aspect of the way the company conducts its business. Having identified these areas it may then be necessary to collect additional information or to conduct detailed forecasts

1. How do you take a view of the future?
   Who is involved?
2. Do you use formal forecasting methods?
   (a) Which?
   (b) How useful are they?

Stable	Evolving	Turbulent
I ——➤ 5	I ——➤ 5	I ——➤ 5

3. Stability of the business environment:
   (a) over past five years
   (b) now
   (c) over next five years
4. Assess each of the following in relation
   to your industry.
   (a) Economic environment:
       availability of finance
       exchange rates
       cost of capital
       etc.
   (b) Technical environment:
       existing technologies
       new technologies
       products
       operational process
       etc.
   (c) Market environment:
       interationalisation
       nature of competition
       segmentation
       etc.
   (d) Social environment:
       life styles
       employee attitudes
       health and safety
       etc.
   (e) Political environment:
       regulation
       product liability
       legislation
       etc.

Now	Future
I ——➤ 5	I ——➤ 5

5. Would you characterise your industry as:
   (a) materials intensive?
   (b) knowledge intensive?
   (c) capital intensive?
   (d) labour intensive?
6. Is the main competitive advantage in your
   industry gained from:
   (a) technical performance?
   (b) price?
   (c) financial incentives, e.g. buy or lease?
   (d) novelty?
   (e) quality?
   (f) service?
7. What is the industry trend for?
   (a) sales volume?
   (b) profit margins?
   (c) return on investment?
8. Is the industry structure:
   (a) a few large companies?
   (b) many small companies?
   (c) a combination of (a) and (b)?
   (d) vertically integrated?
9. Are there any developments in 5-8 above which might represent:
   (a) a major opportunity?
   (b) a significant threat to your company?
10. What are the implication of 5-8 above for the role of technology in your company?

Fig. 8.14 The environmental analysis

in order to evaluate their effect to provide a better basis for decision making.

Conclusion

In this book we have explored the managerial implications of technical change from a variety of viewpoints. Recent developments in technology make it imperative that no company neglect it. For some it may require a reorientation of their strategic thrust. For others the effects may be less dramatic, but it must still be incorporated at a number of levels within the existing operations in order to remain competitive. In all cases there is likely to be a need for some degree of organisational change if the full potential is to be realised. Technical change cannot be divorced from organisational change.

This chapter has described a systematic approach to the analysis of a company's current capability to absorb technical change by means of three audits: the cultural, the innovation and the technical. When compared with the cultural, organisational, managerial and attitudinal requirements which were identified earlier it will reveal that to a lesser or greater extent the current stance of a company is likely to present barriers to its effective implementation. The degree to which technical change is necessary, particularly at the strategic level, can be assessed from the analysis of the business environment of the company and changes occurring in it.

We would not pretend that there is any universal prescription for the successful management of technical change. This must depend upon the company itself, its industry and the nature of the competition. Nevertheless, our experience with many companies attempting to grapple with it indicates that the problems are widespread. The diagnosis of the difficulties encountered shows that many of them could have been avoided if the managers involved had been aware of the experience of others and the considerable volume of research which now exists. Awareness of the characteristics of the process and the removal of barriers do not, of course, ensure success, but they do provide an essential starting point.

Because the ramifications of technical change affect all parts of the business it must be a major concern of top and senior management. However, its implementation demands cooperation from all levels if it is to be effective. This necessitates a greater degree of involvement than has often been the case in the past. Cultural and organisational change is more difficult to effect than the more mechanistic aspects of technical change. Thus they take time. It must be planned carefully and be combined with a programme for education and organisational development.

In conclusion we hope that this book provides a useful introduction to those who are faced with one of the most important problems facing business management today. We should also like to thank the many managers who have contributed to our work and provided us with the opportunity of proving our ideas in real life.

Bibliography

This bibliography gives a selection of books for further reading. It is not intended to be comprehensive. The books do, however, explore in greater depth the issues raised in this text.

Ackoff, R. F. (1981) *Creating the Corporate Future*. Wiley.

Ansoff, H. I. (1984) *Implanting Strategic Information*. Prentice-Hall.

Bartlett, J. B. (1983) *Success and Failure in Quality Circles*. Employment Relations.

Burns, T. and Stalker, G. M. (1961) *The Management of Innovation*. Tavistock Publications.

Daniel, W. W. (1987) *Workplace Industrial Relations and Technical Change*. Frances Pinter.

De Bono, E. (1980) *Opportunities: Handbook of Business Opportunity Search*. Penguin.

Drucker, P. F. (1980) *Managing in Turbulent Times*. Heinemann.

Foster, R. (1986) *Innovation: The Attacker's Advantage*. Macmillan.

Goodridge, M. and Twiss, B. C. (1986) *Management Development and Technological Innovation in Japan*. Manpower Services Commission.

Goodridge, M. and Twiss, B. C. (1988) *Technology, Management and Change*. Manpower Services Commission (In Press)

Goodridge, M. et al. (1988) *Management Training for New Employee Relations Practices*. Training Commission.

Goold, M. and Campbell, A. (1987) *Strategies and Styles*. Blackwell.

Gunn, T. G. (1987) *Manufacturing for Competitive Advantage*. Ballinger.

Handy, C. (1986) *Understanding Organizations*. Penguin.

Harvey-Jones, Sir J. (1988) *Making it Happen: Reflections on Leadership*. Collins.

Hickman, C. R. and Silva, M. A. (1985) *Creating Excellence: Managing Corporate Culture, Strategy and Change in the New Age*. George Allen and Unwin.

Kanter, R. M. (1984) *The Change Masters: Corporate Entrepreneurs at Work*. George Allen and Unwin.

Majaro, S. (1988) *The Creative Gap*. Longman.

NEDC (1988) *Performance and Competitive Success in the UK Electronics Industry*.

Peters, T. (1988) *Thriving on Chaos*. Macmillan.

Peters, T. J. and Waterman, R. H. (1982) *In Search of Excellence*. Harper and Row.

Pinchot, G. (1985) *Intrapreneuring*. Harper and Row.

Porter, M. E. (1980) *Competitive Strategy*. Free Press.

Porter, M. E. (1985) *Competitive Advantage*. Free Press.

Ray, G. F. (1984) *The Diffusion of Mature Technologies*. Cambridge University Press.

Sahal, D. (1981) *Patterns of Technological Innovation*. Addison-Wesley.

Stewart, V. (1983) Change: *The Challenge for Management*. McGraw-Hill.

Twiss, B. C. (1986) *Managing Technological Innovation* (3rd edition). Pitman.

Voss, C. A. (ed.) (1986) *Managing Advanced Manufacturing Technology*. Kempston.

Wall, T. D. (1987) *The Human Side of Advanced Manufacturing Technology*. Wiley.

Index

Acquisitions, 52
Added value, 2, 8
Advanced manufacturing technology, (AMT), 80, 131
Aerospace, 9
Analysis, Environmental, 208, 220–2
Analytical techniques, 185–90
Assertiveness, 196
Assumptions, 134
Attitudes, 181–3
Attributes:
– Product, 6–7, 23–4, 66, 74, 113, 127, 137
– Technical, 115
Audit:
– Cultural, 203–6
– Innovation, 206–17
– Technical, 217–9
Automatic teller machines (ATM), 81
Avery, 66

Barriers, 213, 216
Belbin, 104, 177–8
Benefits:
– Estimation of, 74–6, 134
Biotechnology, 3, 11
Boc, 12
Body scanner, 60
Boeing, 9
Boyatsis, RE, 103

Cambridge science park, 6
Capture, technology, 120
Cash flow, 74, 140–1
Ceramics, 3
Change:
– Assessment of, 13–25
– Need for, 1–25
– Organisational, xv, xvii
– Rate of, 1, 199
– Strategic, 5